Safety Procedures

1. Food or drink is not allowed in the laboratory. Do not eat, drink, apply cosmetics or lip balm in the labs. Do not handle contact lenses. These items could become contaminated.

2. Personal Protective Equipment (PPE) is required while attending lab. Closed toed shoes will be worn during all laboratory periods. Full coverage goggles, long pants to the shoes, long sleeved shirts or lab coats, and protective gloves should be worn while dissecting preserved specimens, handling chemicals or any potentially hazardous materials such as body fluids. Appropriate gloves will be provided in the laboratory. Please notify your instructor of any powder or latex allergies or sensitivities.

3. Do not touch or handle another person's body fluids. In any laboratory activity requiring study of blood, urine or saliva, handle only your own specimens.

4. Dispose of contaminated materials properly. If you are unsure of the procedure, ask your instructor.

5. Do not touch any live specimens without directions from your instructor.

6. Notify your instructor immediately any time an accident occurs. This includes broken glassware, spills of any kind, cuts, scrapes and burns.

7. In the event of a chemical spill move away from the area and notify your instructor immediately. If a chemical is on skin or eyes continuously flush with water for 15 minutes. Remove any contaminated clothing. Wear gloves when cleaning up potentially hazardous substances. Use water to flush the spill area if appropriate.

8. Clean and disinfect laboratory work areas before and at the end of each lab.

9. Wash hands thoroughly before and at the end of each lab period.

10. The fire extinguisher is located on the wall in the main hall just outside the entry/exit door of the lab.

11. Emergency eye wash and shower are located at the back of the lab near the entry/exit door.

12. Exit doors are located at the back of the lab room marked by lighted overhead Exit signs. The entry/exit door opens into the main hallway. The prep room exit door opens into the prep room and then into the main hallway.

13. The emergency telephone is located at the front of the lab room. The College safety number is preprogrammed on the phone. The emergency telephone number is 784-0911.

Verification of Notification and Receipt of Safety Procedures

I acknowledge that I have read the lab Safety Procedures, and that I have received a copy of the lab Safety Procedures to keep in my lab manual for reference.

_____

Student printed name

_____

Student Signature   Date
(Verifies student has read and received a copy of Safety Procedures)

_____

Instructor Signature   Date
(Witnesses student signature and verifies student read and received a copy of Safety Procedures)

TABLE OF CONTENTS

SUGGESTIONS to STUDENTS

Before each lab period, read the entire lab exercise and at least browse through the related textbook chapter examining the illustrations. The lab exercises assume you will always have your textbook with you in lab.

Answer as many questions at the end of the exercise as you possibly can before coming to lab. Most answers to questions will be found in the text of the lab exercise. Some questions intentionally require you to refer to your textbook. All A & P textbooks have a good index at the end. Utilize your textbook's excellent collection of illustrations. One of the key purposes of lab work is to encourage you to integrate what you are learning in the lecture and reading with hands-on activities.

At the end of the lab period your instructor may either require you to hand in the Questions and Observations section for grading or want to check your answers before you leave. Failure to have your work checked may result in loss of credit for that day's work.

MCC Life Science Learning Lab

One set of histology slides, microscopes, bones and most of the models we use in lab are available in this room (SD, NU157 and RM, S154) for supplemental study. The rooms are small and must service all MCC biology students, so the supplies you wish to use may be in use by another student when you drop by. Of course demand is greatest just prior to scheduled lab practical exams. Do not attempt to substitute work in the computer lab for your regular lab work.

We have a variety of instructional tutorials and pretest/post-test programs for this semester's topics available on the lab's computers.

Using the Internet to study anatomy and physiology

Several A & P instructors around the country have prepared and installed supplemental study materials for their students on their WEB sites. Use a search tool such as www.google.com to search for the topic you want to study. You might enter a search word such as mitosis or histology. Examples of some sites students have found useful recently:

> http://www.mesacc.edu/departments/life-science/anatomy-physiology/resources
> http://www.gwc.maricopa.edu/home_pages/crimando/Tutorial_Big.htm
> http://www.kumc.edu/instruction/medicine/anatomy/histoweb/
> http://www.cellsalive.com

As the internet is constantly changing, the above addresses may not be valid when you try them. Please tell your instructor the addresses of sites you find most helpful.

A NOTE ON THE HISTORY OF ANATOMY & PHYSIOLOGY

In May of 2008, I attended Human Anatomy & Physiology Society meetings in New Orleans. We had several workshops that involved the history of our field. I have always been fascinated with history--especially the history of science--and this started me thinking of adding some history to each lab. The following is a brief overview of the main events of the story.

All hunter-gatherer cultures surely knew the anatomy of animals. The shaman would have had a wealth of plants for treatment of disease and injury. Every civilization, including China, India, Japan, Mesopotamia, Egypt, Persia, African civilizations as well as the Incas and Aztecs of the Americas practiced medicine and made observations. Nonetheless, the history of science and medicine today is largely the legacy of the Western world.

The Greeks, of all the ancient civilizations, were the leaders in medicine and anatomy. This is possibly due to their geographical location at the crossroads of Asia, the Middle East, North Africa and Europe. Also, theirs was a culture who fostered inquiry and promotion of basic science. Here, medicine was not only the province of doctors, but also of philosopher-scientists such as Aristotle, Plato and Empedocles.

The "Golden Age" of Greece was approximately from 500-100 BC. **Hippocrates**, the Father of Medicine, was said to have descended from the healing god Aesculapius. The Hippocratic Oath, which speaks of integrity and guidance in medical practice, is often recited by medical school graduates today.

Aristotle, due to his extensive dissection of animals, was the founder of comparative anatomy. He described and named numerous structures and his observations and drawings were remarkably accurate. However, he never dissected a human body and some of his conclusions were in error.

Empedocles is credited with introducing the four elements --fire, air, earth and water-- as the basis of pathology. This idea was further developed by Aristotle to include the four "humors" of blood, yellow bile, black bile and phlegm. According to Aristotle, the four humors were controlled by four organs (the heart, liver, spleen and brain). All illness could be explained by the imbalance of the humors. This led to ideas such as bloodletting and purgatives that persisted well into the 1800s.

When Greece fell to Rome, medical learning continued in Alexandria in northern Egypt. **Herophilus** probably dissected more human bodies than anyone before his time. He restored the brain to its rightful place as the seat of intelligence, rather than the heart, as believed by Aristotle.

During the Roman period (100 BC to 500 AD) another Greek gained special prominence. This was Claudius **Galen**. Born in 129 AD, he was a doctor by age 21. Within a few years he had written books on the uterus, the eye and the chest. He undertook further studies at the medical school at Alexandria and for four years was medical officer to the gladiators. He then went to Rome and won the trust of the emperor, Marcus Aurelius and was physician to his son,

Commodus. (If these names sound familiar, all except Galen himself were in the movie *Gladiator*.)

He was physician to other Roman Emperors as well and his output as a writer was so prolific he kept dozens of scribes occupied. His views on medical science were so completely accepted that after his death, in 201 AD, men stopped doing medical research for more than one thousand years since it was believed that Galen had discovered all there was to know, and further work was futile. Much of his anatomical writings were surprisingly accurate, but not so his physiology. His books, with all the errors they contained, became the medical knowledge learned--by rote memorization-- throughout the Dark and Middle Ages. Even after the Renaissance, many physicians taught in the traditions of Aristotle and Galen could not bring themselves to deny the hallowed words of these revered Greeks.

The time from about 500 to 1100 AD is often called the "Dark Ages". This time included the destruction of Rome by the barbarians and raids by the Vikings who all later came to accept Christianity. The Church services were in Latin as the Christian Church was embraced by the Roman ruler Constantine in 500 AD as he moved the seat of power from Rome to Constantinople.

Unfortunately, in one of the most tragic events in the history of science, the massive library at Alexandria was destroyed. There were many suspects in this destruction, but who destroyed it remains controversial. Western Europe soon found itself in the grip of a tyrannical Church that was totally averse to scientific progress. This lasted until the Renaissance.

Islam was founded in 632 AD and a series of doctors, some Arab, some Jewish, obtained the surviving works of Aristotle, Hippocrates and Galen and kept them safe in Arabic translation in the Middle East. Eventually, they were retranslated into Latin, many by Jewish physicians, and re-introduced to Western Europe. As Latin was the language of learning as dictated by the Church, it, along with Greek, became the language of science and medicine.

The time between 1100 and 1400 AD is termed the Middle Ages. A small resurgence of learning was beginning in Europe. The first medical school in Europe was established in Bologna in 1156 where teaching consisted of reading the re-translations of the Greek works which had been compiled by the Muslim physician **Avicenna.**

Although most science was still controlled by the Christian Church, the Fall of Constantinople in 1453 began to weaken its power.

In the early 1400s, the introduction of printing hastened the Renaissance. During the latter part of this century **Leonardo da Vinci** undertook his dissections and famous accurate and beautiful drawings. Unfortunately, his drawings were lost until the 17th century and therefore had little effect on anatomy during this early time period. By the 16th century, the University of Padua, Italy, had surpassed Bologna. It was here that **Andreas Vesalius**, appointed professor at 23, began to study anatomy by robbing graves and stealing corpses of hanged criminals. In 1543 he completed the monumental anatomical work *De Humanis Corporis Fabrica* (On the Fabric of the Human Body). This work, beautifully illustrated, is still seen as a classic to this day. Unfortunately, his career at Padua lasted only five years as his work was greeted with outrage as

2

it contradicted Galen. Because the Church still frowned on anatomical studies, it is said they imposed a penance on him and he died en route to the Holy Land.

Another significant milestone of the Renaissance was the publication in 1628 of **William Harvey's** classic work on the circulation entitled *Exercitatio Anatomica de Motu Cordis et Sanguinis in Animalibus* (On the Movement of the Heart and Blood in Animals) known to physiologists as *de Motu Cordis*. Although Harvey was trained in the works of Aristotle and Galen, his work relied on human anatomical dissections (no longer forbidden) and experimentation on animals. In his hypothesis that blood completed a circle, powered by the heart he refuted some of the work of Galen. His publication was therefore at first controversial and not accepted well by the medical community.

An essential discovery of the Renaissance was the development of the microscope. **Anton van Leeuwenhoek**, a linen merchant from Holland, not only ground the best microscope lenses of his time in the mid 1600s (up to 270x magnification), but also made many amazing observations and drawings that hold up to this day. Working purely as a hobby, he accumulated 400 microscopes and developed techniques for preparing tissues to be examined. He reported his findings to the Royal Society in London and paved the way for all further microscopic studies.

Now, at last, the complete circuit envisioned by Harvey could be firmly established following the discovery of the microscopic capillaries by **Marcello Malpighi** in 1659.

In the 1630s the Catholic Church was fighting for survival against the Protestant Reformation. Over time, the Church began to further loosen its hold on science. New discoveries now led to more discoveries.

In time, the importance of Harvey's work began to influence medicine and at last physicians thought in terms of physiological function.

This led the way for two other significant events in Anatomy & Physiology that occurred in the mid 1800s. One was the publication in 1858 of British anatomist **Henry Gray's** classic: *Gray's Anatomy of the Human Body*. The other was the work of Frenchman **Claude Bernard**, known as the father of modern physiology. His extensive reliance on observation and experimentation led to many discoveries, including the concept of the "milieu internieur" or "internal environment". The maintenance of this environment is the foundation of homeostasis.

In addition to the history of discoveries, I have tried to give insight to some important **eponyms**. Eponyms are names of the discoverer attached to the structure. This practice flourished in the Middle Ages and the Renaissance largely due to the communication, in Latin, between various scientists. Soon, almost every structure was associated with someone's name.

Towards the end of the 19th century, a revolt began against anatomical eponyms. At the Anatomical Congress of Basel, Switzerland it was decided to use the plain anatomical name first, with the eponym following in parenthesis. This survived in textbooks until 1933 when the Birmingham Revision dispensed with the bracketed names. Finally, in 1955, the Paris Congress decided that eponyms should not be used at all.

However, many names have remained. The most well-known being the Fallopian tube and the Eustachian tube. Many, like the circle of Willis, the loop of Henle and the ampulla of Vater are still used in medicine. Personally, I am sad at their departure as they are a link to history and many have a very interesting story behind them as you will see.

I hope this introduction has given you a brief look at where Anatomy & Physiology has been and how far it has come in such a short time. I hope this will encourage you to find out more about the fascinating history of science.

IMPORTANT!! You signed up to study Anatomy & Physiology, not history. You will <u>not</u> be held responsible for the dates and names unless indicated by your instructor.
B. Kalison, M.S. August, 2008

Some reference I have used. Any errors are my own:

Discovering the Human Body. Bernard Knight, M.D. 1980 Imprint Books

The Last Two Million Years. Readers Digest Association

Medicine an Illustrated History. Albert Lyons, M.D. and Joseph Petrucelli, M.D.

The Anatomical Drawings of Andreas Vesalius. J. Saunders & C. O'Malley. Bonanza Books

Leonardo da Vinci on the Human Body. C. O'Malley & J. Saunders. Crown Publishers.

The Mysteries Within. Sherman Nuland, M.D.

Lectures on the History of Physiology during the 16th, 17th and 18th Centuries.
Sir M. Foster. Dover Publications

BLOOD LAB INFORMATION FORM

I understand that there are a number of viruses, most notably HIV and hepatitis, which can be spread from person to person through blood products. Although the likelihood of such transmission in our laboratory setting is extremely low, certain precautions will, nevertheless, be taken.

I HAVE BEEN INFORMED AS TO THE PROPER SAFETY AND CLEAN UP PROCEDURES REQUIRED FOR THE BLOOD LABS. I UNDERSTAND THAT I AM NOT REQUIRED TO DRAW MY OWN BLOOD AND THAT AN ALTERNATIVE TO THE USE OF HUMAN BLOOD HAS BEEN PROVIDED.

IF I CHOOSE TO WORK WITH HUMAN BLOOD I WILL WORK ONLY WITH MY OWN BLOOD. I UNDERSTAND THAT SAFETY GOGGLES AND GLOVES ARE REQUIRED FOR ALL PROCEDURES. I UNDERSTAND THAT THE COUNTERS ARE TO BE CLEANED BEFORE AND AFTER USE WITH 50% BLEACH. ALL OBJECTS USED IN THIS LAB ARE TO BE DISPOSED OF IN THE BIOHAZARD CONTAINERS.

ANY INCIDENCES OF CONTAMINATION ARE TO BE REPORTED TO THE INSTRUCTOR IMMEDIATELY.

Do not sign the following until your Instructor witnesses your signature.

NAME (PRINT) _____

SIGNATURE _____

DATE _____

INSTRUCTOR'S SIGNATURE _____

DATE _____

BLOOD

HISTORY

Although a few others had observed them, the real credit for the discovery of red blood cells has always been given to the Dutch draper Anton van Leeuwenhoek. As an amateur observer, he ground the lenses of his own microscopes and was somehow able to see such detail that he gave an accurate account of the size of erythrocytes in the year 1674. In 1771, hematologist William Hewson investigated the role of white blood cells. For centuries transfusions were made indiscriminately between humans as well as between animals. Sometimes no ill effects were observed, but often the results were fatal. Dr. Karl Landsteiner of Vienna, Austria undertook a series of experiments where he obtained blood from large numbers of volunteers. In the laboratory he separated cells from plasma and observed the reaction as he mixed cells from one donor with the plasma of another person. He saw the cells agglutinate, or clump, in some cases but not in others. He also tested cells against cells, plasma against plasma and whole blood as well. In 1900, after years of work, he divided human blood into three groups A, B and O. A fourth group, AB, was added later. He received the Nobel Prize for this research in 1930.

OBJECTIVES

1. To determine blood glucose levels using a blood glucose meter.
2. To type blood for ABO and Rh antigens.
3. To determine coagulation (clotting) time.
4. To measure hematocrit.
5. To determine hemoglobin concentration.
6. To determine whodunit in the artificial blood exercise.
7. To identify types of leukocytes and perform a differential count.

I. HUMAN BLOOD

Introduction

Blood is a complex mixture of fluids, solutes, and formed elements. **Formed elements, cells and cell fragments**, comprise about 45% of the blood volume with the remaining portion being plasma. **Plasma** is 91.5% water, 7% proteins, and 1.5% other solutes such as salts, sugars, and gases. The proteins are significant determinates of the blood's osmotic properties. Many of the proteins are antibodies while others are involved in the blood clotting reactions or transportation of materials through the bloodstream. Blood **serum** is plasma without the clotting factors. To prepare serum, blood is allowed to clot before centrifuging to remove both the cells and clotting proteins. **The total volume of blood averages 71.4 ml per kilogram of body weight**.

Blood is vitally involved in a number of the body's homeostatic mechanisms. It is best known for its role as a distribution medium for antibodies, gases, heat, nutrients, water, and other substances. These items are typically picked up at special organs, such as oxygen from the lungs, and carried throughout the body.

Floating in the plasma are three basic types of formed elements. **Erythrocytes**, red blood cells (RBCs), are the most numerous and are red in color due to the hemoglobin they contain. **Hemoglobin** is an iron containing pigment complex which enables the blood to efficiently transport oxygen. **Platelets**, also called thrombocytes, are next in abundance. They are involved in blood clotting. **Leukocytes**, or white blood cells (WBCs), are translucent and must be stained in order to be distinguished. Several types of leukocytes are recognized, each with a distinct nucleus and unique cytoplasmic details. Leukocytes play a vital role in the body's defense against disease by being actively phagocytic or involved in immune processes. A volume of blood normally contains about 1000 times as many erythrocytes as leukocytes.

The study of blood is **hematology**. The results of diagnostic tests on blood are used by health care professionals in evaluating the health and determining the treatment of patients. The procedures we will use were standard clinical practice until automated analytical equipment became widely available in recent years. Now it is possible to introduce a single sample of blood to a machine and program it to run 10, 20 or more diagnostic tests. These manual techniques are still used by the laboratory technicians to calibrate and periodically validate the accuracy of automated equipment. In this exercise our interest is in more than just the results of the tests. Automated machines do not illustrate the diagnostic principles as well as the manual methods do.

Blood Glucose Determination

A common diagnostic test performed on blood is a blood glucose determination. Glucose is a solute dissolved in blood plasma. The amount of glucose in blood is regulated by homeostasis. If there is too little glucose in the blood, **hypoglycemia**, then the brain won't function properly and a person might experience dizziness, mental confusion, loss of consciousness or in extreme cases, death. Persons with too much glucose in the blood, **hyperglycemia**, may experience increased thirst, headaches, and altered mental status all of which may possibly lead to a prolonged loss of consciousness (coma).

Prolonged and chronic hyperglycemia results in a condition called **diabetes mellitus**. There are two distinct forms of diabetes mellitus, Type 1 diabetes mellitus (insulin-dependent, IDDM) and Type 2 diabetes mellitus (non-insulin-dependent, NIDDM). Type 1 diabetes is an auto-immune disease in which the insulin producing cells of the pancreas are destroyed. No insulin is produced and the patient is reliant on insulin injections to regulate their blood glucose levels. Patients that have Type 2 diabetes retain the ability to make insulin, but their cells don't use it well. The likelihood of developing Type 2 diabetes increases if you are 40 years old or older, have a family history of diabetes, and/or you are overweight. Diagnosis of diabetes can be made according criteria set forth by the World Health Organization. Current criteria are either a fasting blood glucose level of greater than 126 mg/dl (7.0 mmol/l), or a blood glucose level greater than 200 mg/dl (11.1 mmol/l) 2 hours after consuming 75 g of glucose. **Normal fasting blood glucose values should be between 70–120 mg/dl (3.9–6.7 mmol/l)**.

Blood Group Typing

Today we know that the blood groups A, B, AB and O, as well as others, are due to the presence of unique antigens and antibodies in each person's blood and that basic mechanisms of immunity are involved in the typing process. The **antigens** or agglutinogens that determine blood type are located on the surface of the erythrocytes. Over 250 different antigens are known. The **antibodies** or agglutinins are in the plasma. Usually before antibodies are produced, it is necessary to be exposed to a foreign antigen. However in the case of the ABO blood groups, the antibodies are genetically determined and are already present at birth. Antibodies cause agglutination of the erythrocytes carrying the corresponding antigen. **Agglutination**, or clumping, of the cells is evidenced by a granular appearance of the blood film on a slide.

The ABO blood type of a person is determined by mixing separate drops of blood with Anti-A antiserum and Anti-B antiserum, which contain the a and b antibodies respectively. Type O blood has neither A nor B antigens and does not react with either antisera. Agglutination with only the Anti-A serum indicates that type A antigens are present on the cells, therefore the blood type is A. Blood type B would agglutinate in the presence of the Anti-B serum. If the blood cells are agglutinated by both Anti-A and Anti-B antisera then the blood is type AB.

The Rh blood type will also be determined. The blood will be tested for only the presence of the D (Rh_O) antigen, which is the most common of more than 40 Rh antigens known. Rh positive (Rh^+) blood reacts with the Anti-D serum. Approximately 85% of the Caucasian population is Rh^+. The other 15% is Rh negative (Rh^-), because their blood does not contain the Rh_O antigen and so does not react with the antiserum. In contrast to the A and B antibodies mentioned above, Rh antibodies are not present at birth. While the capacity to produce them is genetically determined, none will develop until the blood is exposed to Rh^+ antigens. Since we will not test for other Rh factors, such as C and E, you will not know your Rh type with certainty.

Safe transfusions can only occur when the antigenic properties of the donor blood are compatible with the recipient's antibodies. Type A blood may only be given to type A or AB individuals. Conversely, type B blood may only be given to type B or AB individuals. Type O blood may be given to anyone, hence type O individuals are called "universal donors", but type O individuals may only receive from other type O individuals. Rh^+ individuals may receive either Rh^+ or Rh^- blood. Rh^- individuals may only receive from other Rh^- individuals.

Numerous other blood antigens are known and new blood antigens are still being discovered. Blood types are inherited. The mechanisms of their inheritance follow the Mendelian principles that were studied in your prerequisite introductory biology course (Bio181). The relative percentages of the A, B, AB, O, Rh^+ and Rh^- negative blood types varies among the world's racial groups.

Coagulation Time

Hemostasis is a term for the mechanisms involved in the prevention of blood loss. One of the most important hemostatic mechanisms is the process of blood clotting or coagulation. The formation of a blood clot involves a complex series of chemical reactions among substances normally found in the blood and substances released by injured cells and platelets. These reactions result in the polymerization of a blood protein, **fibrin**, and its precipitation to form a fibrous plug or clot. As the clot plugs the vessels at the injury site, **hemorrhage**, or blood loss, is significantly reduced. **The coagulation time normally ranges between 2 and 8 minutes**, and is the time required for a blood sample, removed from the body, to clot.

Hematocrit

The **hematocrit** is the percentage of cells in a volume of blood. A sample of blood is centrifuged to pack the cells and separate them from the plasma. The packed cell volume (PCV) is measured and compared to the total volume of the sample. The PCV is usually considered equivalent to the RBC volume even though a layer of WBCs can be distinguished. WBCs generally constitute about 1% of the total blood volume.

Determination of the hematocrit is simple to perform. It is a reliable test. That is, repeated measurements on a sample from an individual will give consistent results with little variation in readings. A Total Red Cell count is a more precise test, but it is also more complex to perform with results having a higher percentage of error. Thus, hematocrit is the more routine test. A useful correlation exists between hematocrit and the measurement of hemoglobin: the hematocrit value is usually three times the grams hemoglobin/100 ml blood reading.

The normal range of hematocrit, or PCV, values for males is 42 to 52% with a mean of 47%, and for females 37 to 47% with a mean of 42.0%. Fewer cells than normal is diagnosed as **anemia**, while more than normal is considered **polycythemia**.

Determination of the Hemoglobin Content of Blood

Erythrocytes contain about 33% hemoglobin by volume. **Hemoglobin** transports oxygen from the lungs to the tissues and CO_2 from the tissues to the lungs. Hemoglobin is a conjugated protein consisting of a lipid porphyrin compound, containing iron, combined with a protein called globin. The prophyrin compound, known as heme, is composed of four pyrrole rings joined together with methane groups. Iron is suspended in the center of this molecule. Globin, a globulin type of protein, is an aggregate of four polypeptide chains. There are two alpha and two beta chains, each comprised of about 150 amino acids. Each of these chains wraps around a heme molecule. Thus there are four heme units in each hemoglobin molecule, each capable of carrying one oxygen molecule reversibly attached to the ferrous iron. A fully loaded hemoglobin molecule will transport four oxygen molecules. Carbon dioxide is carried by the polypeptide chains rather than the heme.

Each gram of hemoglobin can carry about 1.3 ml of oxygen. The 15 grams of hemoglobin normally found in each 100 ml of blood may contain up to 20 ml of oxygen. In the presence of abundant oxygen, as in the capillaries surrounding the alveoli in the lungs, hemoglobin reacts readily with oxygen forming **oxyhemoglobin** (HbO_2) which is a bright red color. This process is called **oxygenation**. In oxygen deficient surroundings, the HbO_2 dissociates releasing oxygen to the tissues. The blood now becomes dark red in color contributing to the bluish color of your veins.

Numerous methods are available for hemoglobin determination. We will use Tallquist Hemoglobin paper to estimate the amount of hemoglobin in a drop of blood. This technique is not suitable for clinical work. **The average (normal) amount of hemoglobin is 15.6 grams/100 ml blood. The normal range for males is 13 to 18 g/100 ml of blood, for adult females 12 to 16 g/100 ml**. **Anemia** refers to below normal hemoglobin values and implies a reduced ability of the blood to transport oxygen.

Cautions

Usually blood is sterile. But some organisms which cause disease, known as **pathogens,** may enter the infected person's blood. The blood may be contaminated with pathogens and the person is unaware of their infection. Some of these pathogens are extremely virulent and contagious. It is safe for you to handle your own body fluids in a sanitary manner. Today all blood and other body fluids of another person are handled using precautions which assume the fluid contains pathogens.

In today's lab **YOU ARE TO HANDLE ONLY YOUR OWN BLOOD**. You are to sample your own blood and run tests only on your own blood. DO NOT even go near another student's blood! If you help your lab partner, do things that DO NOT require you to contact their blood or to touch items that their blood has contacted.

You will wear surgical nitrile gloves when cleaning up and even when handling items contaminated with your own blood.

Your intact skin is a near perfect barrier to pathogens. Never-the-less, if you should ever accidentally contact another's blood, immediately scrub your hands and the area with soap.

We will be using 50% bleach solution as a disinfectant during this lab. Be careful with it for it can damage your clothing and is hard on the skin.

During this lab you must not be eating or drinking. You are not to handle your contact lenses or apply cosmetics during this lab. If you must leave lab during the period for any reason, remove and discard your gloves putting on a new pair when you return.

Procedures

During this period you are to individually complete five procedures on your blood: blood glucose testing, blood typing, clotting time, hematocrit, and hemoglobin content. Read the all the procedures before coming into lab. Highlight all safety precautions in the procedures and sign the acknowledgement page. Answer the **PRE-LAB QUESTIONS** before coming into lab.

If you choose not to work with blood, contact the instructor. You may then do the "Whodunit" exercise and any other tests on artificial blood as determined by your instructor.

Initial preparation

1. Remove all personal items from the counter top. Remove this lab exercise from your notebook and place it on your chair open to these instructions.

2. Remove any rings with stones or sharp edges and put in your pocket or purse, NOT on the counter. If you cannot remove a sharp ring wrap it with tape to avoid a tear in your gloves. Put on a pair of nitrile gloves and your eye protection and wash down the countertop with the 50% bleach solution and paper towels. 50% bleach solution is harmful to clothing and skin. Discard these paper towels to the trash can. Leave your gloves on, rinse and dry your hands.

3. Place a fresh paper towel on your lab counter. From the supply table gather the following items and place them on the paper towel:
   A. Safety lancet
   B. Alcohol wipe
   C. *Band-Aid*
   D. BLOOD TEST CARD, for blood typing
   E. 4 toothpicks for blood typing and clotting time
   F. Tallquist paper for hemoglobin determination
   G. Heparinized capillary tube, self-sealing

4. Place another clean paper towel on the countertop and then work over it. This will facilitate cleanup at the end of the period as well as improving the visibility of your slides.

5. Locate the Biohazard disposal plastic sharps container and Biohazard bag on the supply table. The safety lancet, toothpicks and capillary tube contaminated with blood are to be placed in the sharps container!! All other materials including gloves and paper towels used in cleanup are to be placed in the Biohazard bag.

6. Remove the glove from the hand you use the least. **Wait until the instructor comes to your group.** While you are waiting, perform the WBC Differential Count.

Test Procedures

1. With YOUR INSTRUCTOR OBSERVING, clean the sides and tip of your middle finger on the hand you use the least using the alcohol wipe. Good blood flow is desirable, and rubbing the finger briskly will increase circulation. When the alcohol has evaporated use the sterile lancet to prick the side of the finger. The instructor will describe the procedure for the use of single use sterile lancet device. A good jab should yield several drops of blood, enough for all tests. DO NOT REUSE a lancet. Use a fresh sterile lancet if an additional puncture is required. Used lancets are to be discarded in the Biohazard sharps container to be sterilized.

2. The first drop of blood should be collected with a blood glucose meter by your instructor. The glucose meter will return a blood glucose reading in less than 10 seconds.

3. Place a drop of blood in each of the three the right hand circles on the BLOOD TEST CARD (Figure 1).

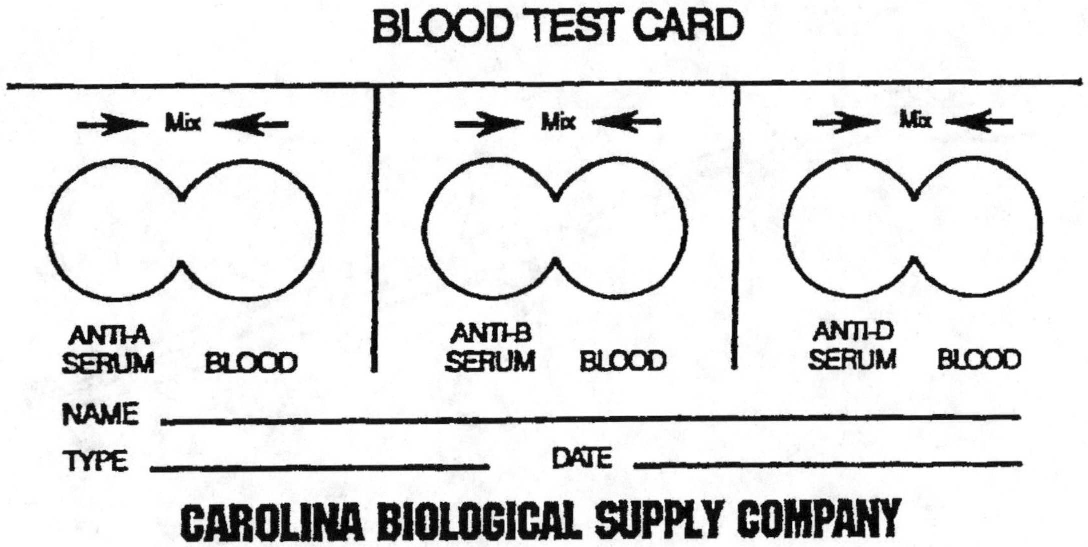

BLOOD TEST CARD

| ANTI-A SERUM | BLOOD | ANTI-B SERUM | BLOOD | ANTI-D SERUM | BLOOD |

NAME _____

TYPE _____ DATE _____

CAROLINA BIOLOGICAL SUPPLY COMPANY

Figure 1. Blood test card

4. Place a fourth drop of blood on a corner of the Blood Test Card and note the time to the second. The drop must be a rounded drop and not a smear. This will be used to determine your clotting time.

5. To determine hematocrit, insert one end of a heparinized capillary tube into a free flowing blood drop from the finger puncture (Figure 2). Hold the tube tilted slightly downward. (Gravity is your friend.) Fill the tube at least half full. When the blood contacts the seal, no more blood can be taken into the tube and the tube self-seals. When the tube is full and the blood is not touching the seal, hold the tube in one hand and pound that hand into the other hand until the blood does touch the seal. Lay the tube flat on your paper towel.

   Squeezing on the finger to encourage blood flow may be necessary to obtain sufficient blood for the tests. However, squeezing changes the plasma to cell proportions in the drop; altering the accuracy of the hematocrit results.

6. Place your last drop of blood on the Tallquist paper for hemoglobin determination.

7. Blot the blood off your finger with the alcohol wipe and apply the *Band Aid*. Put the glove back on this hand.

8. The instructor will place small drops (1/4" diam.) of Anti-A, Anti-B, and Anti-D serums on the left circles of the BLOOD TEST CARD. The blood typing drops need to be mixed with

the anti-sera immediately, otherwise the clotting reactions of the blood will confuse the determination of agglutination.

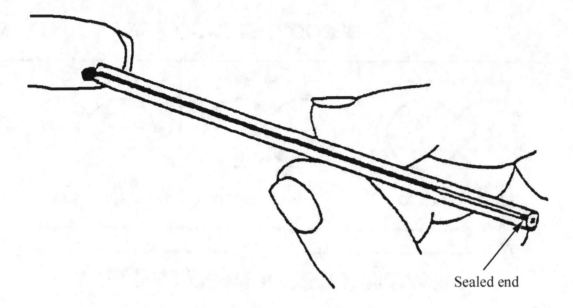

Sealed end

Figure 2. Blood collection into a heparinized capillary tube for hematocrit determination

A. With your glove on, use a separate toothpick to mix each of the antisera with its blood drop.

B. Use the flat of the toothpick and smear in a windshield wiper fashion.

C. DO NOT allow the different antisera/blood puddles to run together.

D. Observe the BLOOD TEST CARD for agglutination. **Agglutination** is the clumping of the cells into small groups. Agglutination should be evident within one minute of mixing of the blood and antisera. Determinations must be completed before the blood dries.

Agglutination can be seen with the unaided eye. The degree of clumping will vary from individual to individual due to variation in the antigens. The D antigen gives a weaker response than the A or B antigens. A positive reaction is indicated by a granular appearance of the blood film, no matter how slight.

If the blood and antisera remain homogeneous in your samples, no reaction occurred, and the blood is type O and the Rh factor is negative. Record your blood types on the board.

E. Place the BLOOD TEST CARD in the biohazard bag and toothpicks in the Sharps container.

9. Determine Blood Clotting time.

   A. Starting 30 seconds after the drop used for clotting time determination first appeared; drag a toothpick slowly through the puddle of blood.

   B. Lift it slightly at the end of the drop to look for strands of fibrin clinging to the tip.

   C. Repeat the process with the toothpick at 30 second intervals until the fine fibrin threads are detected on the toothpick. This is the end point, note the time. This is your coagulation (clotting) time!

   D. Used toothpicks are to be discarded in the Sharps container.

10. Determine hematocrit.

   A. Pick up the capillary tube and place the tube, with the sealed end pointing outward, into one of the radial grooves in the microhematocrit centrifuge. Remember the number of the groove that you placed your tube into.

   B. The instructor will centrifuge the tubes when the centrifuge is full.

   C. The hematocrit may be read directly using the cards provided. Align the bottom of the blood column with 0. Slide the scale until the 100% line is at the top of the blood column. Read the % PCV using the scale. If your sample is too small to measure by this method, see the instructor who will measure the column of red cells using a millimeter ruler and divide this distance by the total length of the blood column. Multiply this quotient by 100 to obtain the percentage of red blood cells.

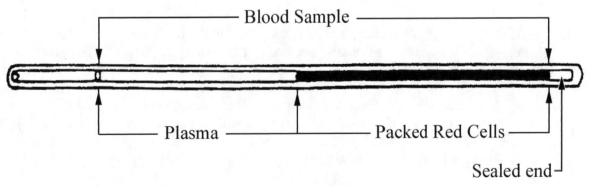

Figure 3. Filled heparinized capillary tube after centrifugation.

11. When the drop of blood on the Tallquist paper has lost its wet gloss, compare it with the color chart provided to determine the approximate hemoglobin content of your blood. Write your hemoglobin levels on the white board so class averages can be obtained for each sex.

12. CLEAN UP YOUR WORK SPACE. You should still have on your gloves and goggles. Place the paper towel containing the BLOOD TEST CARD, toothpicks, hematocrit tube, Tallquist paper, lancets, and wipes in the Biohazard plastic Sharps container.

13. Wash down the countertop with 50% bleach using fresh paper towels, discarding towels to the trash. 50% bleach solution is harmful to clothing and skin. Pull off your gloves so that the outside is now inside, discarding in the Biohazard disposal bag. Wash your hands with soap and water.

II. WHODUNIT EXERCISE (OPTIONAL) To be done if you finish early or if you are using artificial blood.

With the exception of identical twins, each person's tissues including their blood and ear wax have some unique compounds, most often proteins. Our chromosomes have segments with unique nucleotide sequences. Since members of a species have more in common than they do differences, it is often difficult and costly to assay and identify the uniqueness to the individual level. The antigens for blood types can be use to place individuals in groups but cannot be used to precisely identify individuals. The identification of a combination of blood antigens is a common tool used by forensic science to eliminate or link a suspect to blood at a crime scene.

In this exercise you and your lab partners are the forensic technicians. You have blood from the victim and have collected blood from the car seat where the crime occurred. Detectives have just brought you blood samples from four suspects.

Procedure

1. Obtain 6 of the small plastic trays and label them: victim, crime scene, suspect 1, 2, 3, and 4. This exercise uses synthetic materials. You do NOT need to wear gloves for this procedure, unless you want to practice putting on and taking off gloves.

2. Place 3 drops of an artificial blood sample in each of the tray's 3 cells. Insure that the correct blood sample is placed in the appropriate tray. You will have a tray with blood for each of the 6 sources. The cells are labeled A, B, and Rh. Add 3 drops of the blue anti-A serum to the proper blood pool. Add the yellow anti-B and green anti-Rh to the appropriate cells.

3. Rock the trays back and forth to mix the blood and antisera, waiting a few minutes for a gel to form. This is NOT true agglutination, so it will not look like your blood typing reactions. The artificial blood reaction with the anti-B antisera is slower. If no reaction occurs, the mixtures retain a uniform red translucent appearance.

4. Determine the blood types for each of your 6 specimens and record.

III. IDENTIFICATION OF LEUKOCYTES AND DIFFERENTIAL COUNT

Introduction

Blood cells are best seen in a thin smear of a blood droplet. Then only the **erythrocytes** can be distinguished because the **leukocytes** and **platelets** lack pigment. To enhance the visibility of all the cells we treat the smear with a **differential stain** such as Wright's stain, a mix of various dyes. The chemicals in this stain improve the visibility of erythrocytes and stain the cytoplasm of the various leukocytes different colors. The nuclei of all leukocytes will stain dark blue or purple. The erythrocytes should appear pale red. We will use blood smears which have been professionally prepared to study the morphology of leukocytes and to perform a differential count of white blood cells.

The leukocytes reacted differentially with the components of the stain permitting us to distinguish different morphological types. It has long been assumed that the different structural types were specialized for unique functions. This view is supported by the observation that numbers of certain cells increase in response to specific diseases. This cause/effect relationship enables the physician to use the differential white cell count as a diagnostic tool.

The differential stain makes tiny granules visible in the cytoplasm of many leukocytes. Depending on the cell, the granules may stain blue, purple, pink, red, orange or some combination of colors. We now know these granules to be cell vesicles containing unique enzymes and other chemicals which the cell uses in defense work. As the various cell types are described, brief references will be made to their association with specific diseases. Compare the descriptions below with the illustrations in your textbook.

1. **Erythrocytes** (red blood cells = RBCs) are the most abundant cells present. **A normal red cell count for adult males ranges from 4.7 to 6.1 million cells per cubic millimeter (µl). Females normally have 4.2-5.4 million cells per cubic millimeter (µl).** Lower than normal counts indicate **anemia**. Higher than normal counts indicate **polycythemia**. RBCs appear as small, 8 microns (µm) diameter, light orange round biconcave discs. These anucleate cells have the shape of a doughnut with membranes stretched across the hole. If the surface of the RBCs on your slide appear to be rough with little projections on their surface they are **crenated** or shrunken. Crenation is most often caused by the smear being dried too slowly. Erythrocytes transport both oxygen and carbon dioxide for us. To estimate size, other structures are often compared to the 8 µm diameter RBC.

2. **Leukocytes** (white blood cells = WBCs) all have a nucleus. **A normal white cell count should range from 4,000 to 10,800 WBCs per cubic millimeter (µl).** Low counts are termed leukopenia. High counts are termed leukocytosis. Most leukocytes are larger than erythrocytes. Leukocytes are produced at about the same rate as erythrocytes but they have a shorter lifespan and also tend to migrate out of the blood stream. In the red bone marrow the different types of WBCs develop from a common precursor cell. They normally complete their differentiation and maturation in the marrow before being thrown out into the blood stream. However some of these little urchins hit the "street" before they

are mature. Do not trouble yourself trying to identify cells that do not fit into the categories described below.

A. **Lymphocytes** (25-40% of all leukocytes) are usually about 9-10 μm in diameter. The single large nucleus is nearly spherical in shape and stains the typical dark purple. The nucleus nearly fills the cell leaving just a narrow band of light blue cytoplasm surrounding it. Lymphocytes are especially common in the lymph system as well as the blood. They are able to move by diapedesis/emigration among the cells of other tissues particularly connective tissues. They are known to be active in the immunity process and are suspected to be able to transform themselves into other types of cells. We know that some lymphocytes, the B cells, become plasma cells which produce antibodies. A few lymphocytes may be seen that are twice as big as a RBC. Increased numbers of lymphocytes have been associated with infections such as whooping cough and some viral infections.

B. **Monocytes** (3-8% of all leukocytes) are large cells, 14-19 μm, with more abundant cytoplasm than lymphocytes. Their nucleus is often shaped like a kidney bean or a C. They are actively phagocytic and respond to injury and invasions of foreign antigens on a long term basis. Monocytes in the tissues are called macrophages. They wander throughout the intercellular regions looking for invaders! Increased counts of monocytes are related to prolonged or chronic infections such as tuberculosis and mononucleosus.

C. **Neutrophils** (50-70% of leukocytes) usually have a nucleus with 3-5 interconnected lobes; hence the term **polymorphonuclear leukocyte** is often used in reference to these cells. The neutral component in Wright's stain dyes the tiny droplets (-*phil* = loving) in the cytoplasm a light pink producing a granular appearance. Neutrophils are the most active WBC responding to pus forming infections, those caused by bacteria. The phagocytic actions of neutrophils are an important component of the body's non-specific defenses. An elevated neutrophil count can be a clue to an internal bacterial infection such as appendicitis. Diseases such as typhoid fever, undulant fever and influenza are associated with marked decreases in numbers of neutrophils. Banded, immature, neutrophils may appear in the blood and are easily confused with monocytes. When in doubt call the cells neutrophils. The ratio of banded to mature polymorphonuclear cells in the circulating blood gives a clue as to the speed of cell production in the marrow.

D. **Eosinophils** (1-4% of leukocytes) usually have a bilobed nucleus which may be difficult to see due to the abundant deeply stained red granules. The cytoplasmic vesicles are reacting with ("loving") eosin, an acid component of Wright's stain. Both neutrophils and eosinophils are 10-12 μm in diameter. An elevated eosinophil count often indicates a parasitic infection or an allergic reaction.

E. **Basophils** (0.5-1% of leukocytes) are smaller, 8-10 μm, cells whose cytoplasmic vesicles are large, abundant and deeply stained by the dark blue basic dyes. The nucleus is usually hidden from view by the granules, but if seen will be bilobed or U-shaped. Basophils are involved in allergic reactions. Basophils and mast cells share a similar appearance and both are thought to produce heparin, histamine and other chemicals. In spite of these similarities, most authorities consider them to be independent cell types.

Lymphocytes and monocytes are often grouped together as **agranular leukocytes** because their cytoplasmic vesicles do not pick up the dyes in Wright's stain very well. Thus "granules" are not obvious. **Granular leukocytes** include the neutrophils, eosinophils and basophils with obvious vesicles or granules.

3. **Platelets** or **Thrombocytes** result from the fragmentation of giant cells called *megakaryocytes*, a type of WBC in the marrow. Thus, platelets are not true cells, only cell fragments but with a surrounding membrane. A cubic millimeter of blood should contain 150,000-400,000 platelets. They are usually seen in clusters of 10-20. Each platelet is dark staining and less than a quarter the diameter of a RBC. When platelets contact injured cells or collagen fibers they release some phospholipids which initiate the blood clotting reactions.

Procedure

Goggles and gloves are not needed when working with the prepared blood smear slides.

You are to learn to confidently identify the various types of blood cells. This skill is required before performing the **differential WBC count**. You will need your textbook illustrations.

1. Observe the slide, prepared with Wright's stain, under scanning and then low power magnification and select a region where the cells are spread out, not stacked on one another. This will usually be an area toward the one end of the slide. Scan and note the uniform distribution of the white cells among the RBCs. If the slide seems to have more WBCs along the sides of the smear it was not ideally prepared. A slide like this can be used to identify the WBCs but may result in an inaccurate differential count. Obtain a better one to use for the differential count.

2. Once you have located a good area switch to 40X to examine a few leukocytes attempting to identify them. Distinguishing lymphocytes and neutrophils should be easy. Roam around the slide looking for white blood cells, concentrating on seeing as much detail as you can with the 40X objective. First move to the upper left corner of the area you found with a good cell distribution.

3. Use a zig-zag search pattern to prevent counting any cell twice (Figure 4). As you move around, identify each WBC encountered and tally it on the chart in the POST-LAB OBSERVATIONS section. PATIENTLY look until you have counted 100 white cells. For each cell type determine its proportion or percentage of the total.

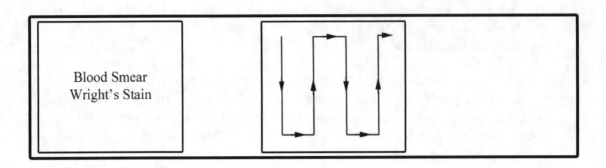

Figure 4. Zig-zag pattern used to find white blood cells and avoid duplicate counting during a WBC differential count.

In past years, the students also performed a **Total Red Cell count** and a **Total White Cell count**. They did this by diluting the blood with special diluting chambers and placing the diluted blood on a special counting slide called a **hemocytometer**. Under the microscope, the following grid appeared. For the red cell count the student would count all the cells in the areas marked with R, then add them up and multiply by the dilution factor. For the white cells, a separate diluting fluid was used and the students would count all the white cells in the four areas marked with a W. They would then multiply this count by the correct dilution factor.

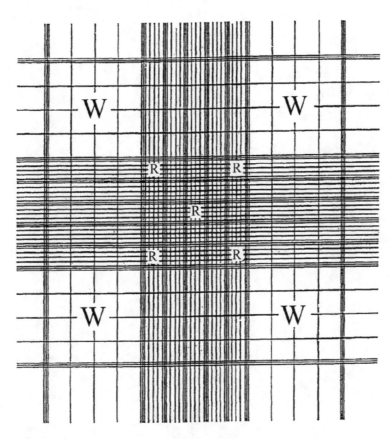

Figure 5. Grid layout on a hemocytometer. Count all white blood cells in the squares marked "W" during a total white blood cell count. Count all red blood cells in the squares marked "R" during a total red blood cell count.

PRE-LAB QUESTIONS   Name _____

A. Define the following terms by reading this lab:

1. hematology

2. hematocrit

3. antibody

4. antigen

5. anemia

6. agglutination

7. polycythemia

8. plasma

9. serum

10. hyperglycemia

B. Complete the table.

Blood Type	Antigens on RBC surface	Antibodies in plasma	Can receive blood from:	Can donate blood to: *
A				
B				
AB				
O				

*Remember: the antibodies in the recipient's blood will 'attack' the donated specimen's antigens if they are similar such as A antibodies agglutinating A antigens. The antibodies present in the donated specimen are of less concern, since they will be greatly diluted once mixed with the host's blood plasma and thus will not cause any significant hemolysis of the recipient's RBCs.

C. Fill In and Discussion

1. How is serum prepared?

2. What is hemoglobin?

3. If you had a high hematocrit, would you expect your total RBC count to also be high? _____ Why?

4. If type A blood was transfused to a type B person who has anti A antibodies would you expect a reaction between the two bloods? _____ Describe the expected reaction.

5. The first time type Rh^+ blood was transfused to a type Rh^- person would you expect an immediate reaction between the two bloods? _____

6. What is the difference in the Rh and ABO blood groups and their antibodies that allows the transfusion in #5 to be safe the first time while that in #4 is never safe?

7. Define and distinguish between agglutination and clotting.

8. Where should you place the blood card, toothpicks, lancets and hematocrit tubes after use?

From the History
9. What research led to a Nobel Prize for Karl Landsteiner?

10. What is the name of the special counting slide that could have been used to determine Total red blood cell and Total white cell counts if we had used it?

11. Use your textbook or MCC's Anatomy website to draw and color pictures representative of each leukocyte type.

12. What are some symptoms of hypoglycemia?

13. Describe the differences between Type 1 and Type 2 diabetes mellitus.

14. Matching:

                a. erythrocyte   e. monocyte
                b. megakaryocyte   f. neutrophil
                c. platelet   g. eosinophil
                d. lymphocyte   h. basophil

_____ are called macrophages in the tissues

_____ RBCs

_____ releases histamine during allergic reactions

_____ an elevated count often indicates a parasitic infection

_____ are known to be active in the process of immunity, some are called B cells

_____ responds to pus forming infections

_____ involved in initiating blood clotting

_____ the least common type of WBC

_____ _____ agranular leukocytes

_____ _____ _____ granular leukocytes

_____ very active phagocytic cells important in non-specific defenses

_____ source of platelets in the marrow

_____ contain hemoglobin

_____ most abundant WBC with a 3 to 5 lobed nucleus

POST-LAB OBSERVATIONS

I. HUMAN BLOOD

Blood Glucose Determination

A. My Blood Glucose Value _____ mg/dl

Blood Group Typing

A. My blood type: ABO blood group _____ Rh group _____

B. Tabulate class data

	A	B	AB	O
Rh$^+$				
Rh$^-$				

Coagulation Time

A. My blood coagulated in _____

Hematocrit

A. My hematocrit: _____

B. Is this value within the normal range? _____

C. A quick estimate of the hemoglobin value is one third the hematocrit value.
      hematocrit value / 3 = your hematocrit / 3 = _____g/100 mL

Determination of the Hemoglobin Content of Blood

A. My hemoglobin: _____ grams hemoglobin / 100 ml blood

B. Is this within the normal range for your sex? _____

C. How does this value compare to the value calculated at the end of the *Hematocrit* section?

D. Using the data for the class tabulated on the board, calculate the average hemoglobin values
      for:
            Males _____   Females _____

II. WHODUNIT EXERCISE (OPTIONAL)

A. Blood types:

Victim _____   Crime scene _____

Suspect 1 _____   Suspect 2 _____

Suspect 3 _____   Suspect 4 _____

B. Is the crime scene blood that of the victim? _____

C. Which of the Suspects' blood matches that of the crime scene? _____

D. Explain why this evidence linking the suspect to the crime does NOT prove guilt.

E. Provide some other explanations for blood being present that provisionally matches that of one of the suspects?

III. IDENTIFICATION OF LEUKOCYTES AND DIFFERENTIAL COUNT

A. In the first row of spaces in the table tally with hatch marks the various WBCs as you locate and identify them. Write the count as a number in the second row and calculate a percentage of the total observed for the third row.

	Neutrophil	Eosinophil	Basophil	Lymphocyte	Monocyte
Tally					
Count					
Percentage					
Normal %					

B. **Discuss** in writing how your differential count compares to the normal values accounting for differences.

BIO 202 Blood lab exercise

I have read the entire lab exercise before coming to lab. I have highlighted the safety precautions in the procedures sections.

Signature _____ Date _____

I have completed the Blood Lab. I have complied with all safety instructions both written and oral from the instructor.

Signature _____ Date _____

If you experienced a problem or had an accident with the procedures in the blood lab, write a description of the problem below.

HEART ANATOMY

HISTORY

The Chinese had the action of the heart correct in the classic work the *Nei Ching* in the third century B.C. without the benefit of dissection. The West would not have the function of the heart correct until the seventeenth century. Aristotle did place the heart at the center of all vital processes, and believed it was the seat of intelligence. Many since have thought it seat of the soul. Claudius Galen in the second century A.D. believed the liver was more important than the heart. He said that blood entered the right side of the heart through the vena cava. Here, it gave up the impurities from the tissues. It did so by making its way through small "pores" in the interventricular septum to mix with the "pneuma" which entered the left side of the heart through the windpipe. The supposed existence of these pores was taught as fact for centuries and even Leonardo Da Vinci drew in the non existent pores in his work because Galen said they were there. William Harvey finally correctly described the function of the heart in his monumental work on circulation in 1628. Even then, he feared the consequences of going against the revered Galen.

OBJECTIVES

1. Study the anatomy of the human heart.
2. Study the anatomy of a sheep or pig heart.
3. Study the histology of cardiac muscle.

I. HUMAN HEART ANATOMY - HEART MODELS

Introduction

The parts of the circulatory system you will be studying lie within the body cavity, or **coelom**. In mammals, including humans, a muscular **diaphragm** divides the body cavity into a superior **thoracic cavity** and an inferior **abdominal cavity**. The human heart rests on the diaphragm, with its apex pointing anteriorly, slightly off center to the left at about the level of the fifth intercostal space. The heart is located in an area in the middle of the thoracic cavity called the **mediastinum**, which includes the thymus gland, heart and all other thoracic structures except the lungs. The mediastinum separates the right pleural cavity containing the right lung from the left one. Posterior to the heart is the esophagus, aorta and vertebral column. Anterior to the heart is the thymus gland and sternum.

The human heart, as well as those in all other mammals and birds, is divided into four chambers, two **atria** and two **ventricles**. Blood returns from the body to the **right atrium** through two large veins, the **superior vena cava** and the **inferior vena cava**, to be forced by the **right ventricle** through the **pulmonary arteries** to the lungs for oxygenation. Blood flows into the **left atrium** from the lungs through the **pulmonary veins** and then is pumped by the **left ventricle** through the **aorta** to all parts of the body, except the lungs. The right and left sides of the heart are in terms of the organ's natural anatomical position, not that of the observer. (This is true of all other anatomical structures as well!) Between the atria and ventricles you will find a groove called the **coronary sulcus**.

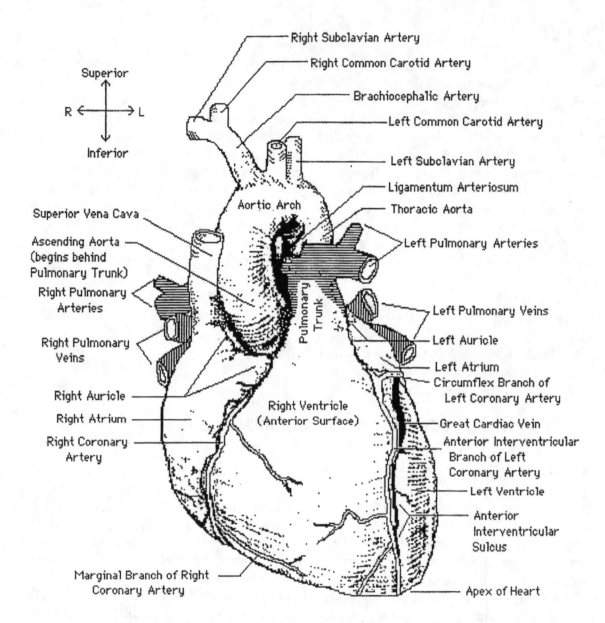

Figure 1. Human Heart, Anterior external view. In life the cardiac veins parallel and often overlie the coronary arteries. Both vessels are often covered with adipose tissue. Most of the left ventricle is posterior, while most of the heart's anterior and diaphragmatic surfaces are the right ventricle.

The heart is enclosed by a tough **pericardial sac**. The outer layer of this sac is a fibrous membrane anchored to several structures of the mediastinum. The inside of this sac is lined with a smooth serous membrane, the **parietal pericardium**. This membrane continues over the outer surface of the heart as the **visceral pericardium** (also called the **epicardium**). These smooth moist membranes minimize friction as the heart moves with each beat. You must study the

Heart 2- 2

illustrations in your textbook to see the structures of the mediastinum and pericardial sac since they are not on the models. You may, however, see them on the sheep or pig heart.

Like all tissues in the body, there are blood vessels that supply the heart with nutrients. **Coronary arteries** supply the heart with blood. The **right and left coronary arteries** branch from the aorta. The right coronary artery runs anteriorly to the right side of the heart following the **coronary sulcus**. The right coronary artery branches into the **marginal** and **posterior interventricular branches**. The **left coronary artery** runs anteriorly to the left side of the heart. It divides into two main branches. The **anterior interventricular branch** descends across the anterior surface of the heart. This branch is also known as the anterior descending branch. It supplies both the right and left ventricle's anterior walls. The anterior interventricular branch of the left coronary artery is the "most important" coronary artery, because of the large and functionally important heart areas supplied. It is also the one most commonly blocked by atherosclerotic plaques, usually at branching points. Blockage of coronary arteries with fatty deposits deprives the heart cells of oxygen and nutrients and is the common cause of **myocardial infarction**, heart attack. By far, most coronary bypass surgeries and myocardial infarctions are associated with this particular vessel. The **circumflex branch** of the left coronary artery follows the coronary sulcus between left atrium and ventricle around to the posterior side of the heart, supplying nearby structures along its path.

For the most part the veins draining the heart parallel the arteries and are called **cardiac veins**. The **great cardiac vein** drains the anterior portion of the heart running parallel to the anterior interventricular branch of the left coronary artery. The **middle cardiac vein** lies alongside the posterior interventricular branch of the right coronary artery and drains the posterior aspect of the heart. The cardiac veins all feed into the **coronary sinus** lying in the coronary sulcus on the posterior side of the heart. The coronary sinus has no smooth muscle in its wall and thus cannot change its diameter. The sinus opens into the right atrium near the inferior vena cava's opening.

During fetal development, very little blood goes to the lungs. The blood is diverted from the right atrium to the left atrium through a hole in the inner heart wall called the foramen ovale, bypassing the right ventricle. Most of the blood entering the pulmonary trunk was shunted into an artery, the ductus arteriosus, which leads to the aorta, bypassing the lungs. After birth, both of these structures close. The foramen ovale will become the **fossa ovalis**, which is found in the right atrium and the ductus arteriosus will become the **ligamentum arteriosum** connecting the pulmonary trunk with the aorta.

Procedure

1. Consult Figure 2 to see the projection of the heart outline to the surface. Compare the diagram to the human torso model and then palpate the four corner landmarks on your own chest. We will refer to this outline again when we listen for heart sounds.

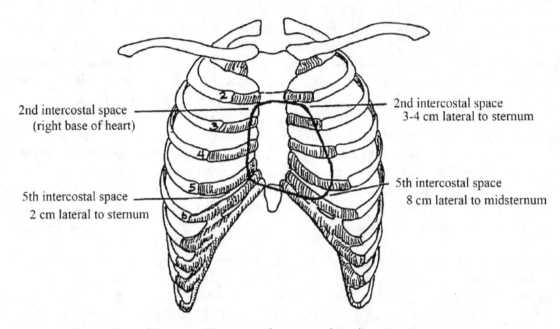

2nd intercostal space
(right base of heart)

2nd intercostal space
3-4 cm lateral to sternum

5th intercostal space
2 cm lateral to sternum

5th intercostal space
8 cm lateral to midsternum

Figure 2. Projection of heart outline to surface, anterior view

2. Locate and identify all the structures listed in the table on the heart models. We have several different heart models. Not all structures are shown on the smaller models, so you will need to eventually look at each of the different models. Please consult your textbook if you are having trouble identifying any of the structures.

3. Fill in the diagrams in the POST-LAB OBSERVATIONS section.

Key to the Heart Models

Structure Name	Medium Heart	Large Heart
superior vena cava	1	1
inferior vena cava	2	2
right auricle	3	3
pectinate muscle (inside the walls of both auricles)	4	4
right atrium	5	5
fossa ovalis (in right atrium)	6	6
opening of the coronary sinus (seen below right atrium)	7	7
tricuspid valve (= right atrioventricular valve = right AV valve)	8	8
chordae tendineae	9	9
papillary muscles	10	10
right ventricle	11	11
trabeculae carneae	12	12
interventricular septum	13	13
pulmonary semilunar valves	14	14
pulmonary trunk	15	15
left pulmonary artery	16	16
right pulmonary artery	17	17
left pulmonary veins	18	18
right pulmonary veins	19	19
left auricle	20	20
left atrium	21	21
bicuspid valve (= mitral valve = left atrioventricular valve = left AV valve)	22	22
left ventricle	23	23
aortic semilunar valve	24	24
ascending aorta	25	25
aortic arch	26	26
thoracic aorta	28	28
ligamentum arteriosum	29	29
brachiocephalic artery	30	30
left common carotid artery	31	31
left subclavian artery	32	32
coronary sulcus	33	33
right coronary artery	34	34
marginal branch of right coronary artery	35	35
posterior interventricular branches of right coronary artery	36	36
left coronary artery	37	37

Structure Name	Medium Heart	Large Heart
anterior interventricular branch of left coronary artery (=left anterior descending artery=LAD)	38	38
anterior interventricular sulcus	39	39
circumflex branch of left coronary artery	40	40
apex of heart	41	41
coronary sinus	42	42
great cardiac vein	43	43
middle cardiac vein	44	44
right common carotid artery		45
right subclavian artery		46
left brachiocephalic vein		47
right brachiocephalic vein		48
left internal jugular vein		49
right internal jugular vein		50
left subclavian vein		51
right subclavian vein		52
esophagus		59
trachea		60
right bronchus		61
left bronchus		62
azygos vein		64

Common areas of confusion:

1. The term **atrium** (plural=atria) refers to the chamber inside. The term **auricle** refers to the ear-like projection on the outside that makes the atrium larger.

2. Arteries are usually colored red and veins are usually colored blue on the models. Exceptions are that the **pulmonary arteries are blue and the pulmonary veins are red**. This is because most arteries carry blood rich in oxygen that is bright red and most veins carry oxygen poor blood that is dark red. Arteries are defined as vessels that carry blood away from the heart. In the pulmonary system case, blood is going to the lungs to get oxygen through arteries. Veins are defined as vessels that bring blood back to the heart. In the case of the pulmonary veins, they come back from the lungs rich in oxygenated blood.

II. SHEEP OR PIG HEART ANATOMY

Introduction

You are expected to study both the models of the human heart and the sheep/pig heart. A healthy human heart is only slightly larger than the sheep heart. You will notice that the sheep/pig heart is more conical. In the sheep's/pig's chest the heart's apex points posteriorly as the heart rests on the sternum. Upright posture in the human caused the heart to shift and ride on the diaphragm, flattening and slightly bending the cone shape. In a four legged animal, anterior is called **ventral** and posterior is called **dorsal.**

Procedure

1. Put on nitrile gloves and collect a dissection tray, scissors, blunt probe, forceps and scalpel.

2. Obtain a sheep/pig heart from the 5 gallon bucket under the hood and place in a dissection tray that is lined with paper towels to ease later clean up.

3. At the sink rinse with water to flush away preservatives; run water through the great vessels as well as over the surface. While the preservatives may not smell like roses they are not considered toxic to the skin. However, if you are pregnant we recommend you limit your contact with any strange chemicals including preservatives considered safe to others.

4. The heart may or may not have the pericardium intact. You must study the illustrations in your textbook to see the structures of the mediastinum and pericardial sac if the pericardium has been removed. If the pericardium is intact, there may be considerable fat outside the parietal pericardium and part of the thymus may be attached. Take the time to determine how tough and fibrous the pericardial sac is!

5. Determine which end of the heart is superior and which is inferior. Look for all of the blood vessels. They are superior. The other end is the inferior **apex**, the conical end of the heart. It was near the diaphragm. The major vessels enter and leave the heart at the **base**. Of course the base is broader than the apex.

6. Remove the pericardium by cutting through it near the apex of the heart. Then peel the heart out of the pericardium like you would peel a banana, drawing the pericardium superiorly and turning it inside out at the same time. Cut the pericardium away from the heart and blood vessels with a sharp scissors. The smooth shiny surface on the inside of the pericardium is the **parietal pericardium**. The smooth shiny surface on the surface of the heart is the **visceral pericardium**. Both are made of simple squamous epithelial tissue with a thin layer of connective tissue underlying the epithelium and connecting it to the muscle. The visceral pericardium is often referred to as the **epicardium**. Remember, these smooth moist membranes slide past one another and minimize friction as the heart moves with each beat. Take a probe, prick the surface of the heart and try to lift away a bit of the visceral pericardium, or epicardium, to verify its existence. It cannot, however, be removed. Set aside the pericardium to be disposed of later.

7. Look at your heart and observe the yellow masses of fat. They lie between the visceral pericardium and cardiac muscle of the heart wall. This may make it difficult to see the major coronary arteries and veins. However you do not need to remove this fat.

8. Around the great vessels there is some fat outside the pericardium. Clear any fat away from the great vessels using a careful scraping scalpel or, best yet, a series of paper towels. Show the heart to your instructor once the fat has been cleared away.

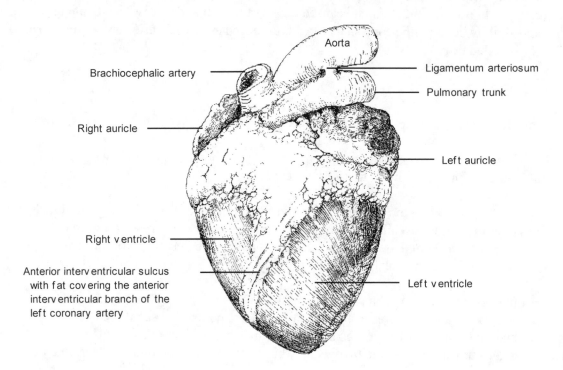

Figure 3. Sheep heart, ventral view.

9. Identify the blood vessels emerging from the heart at the base. Identification of the vessels will be more difficult if the butcher cut them off close to the heart. If you know which vessels are attached to which heart chamber, then you can identify an unknown vessel by determining which chamber it drains or feeds. Use the blunt handle of the dissecting probes to probe into a vessel.

    a. The most prominent vessel ventrally is the **pulmonary trunk**. Locate this vessel.

    b. The pulmonary trunk divides into the **right and left pulmonary arteries** which then go to the right and left lungs. The pulmonary arteries were cut from most of the hearts we see.

    c. The **aorta** is usually, but not always, the largest diameter vessel with the thickest walls you will find on the heart. It is located dorsal to the pulmonary trunk. If the aorta is not cut too short you will be able to see the first part of the **aortic arch** before it becomes the **thoracic aorta**.

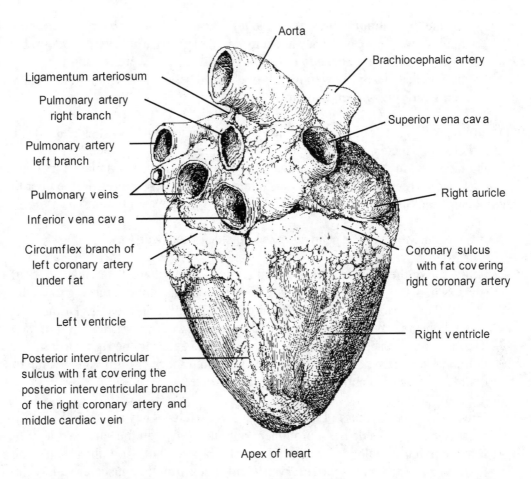

Figure 4. Sheep heart, dorsal view.

d. The **brachiocephalic** (also called the innominate) **artery** is the first big branch off the aorta. It will be seen superior and to the right of the pulmonary trunk. The human heart has three branches off the aortic arch: the brachiocephalic, left common carotid, and left subclavian arteries. In the pig and cat there are only two branches because the **left common carotid** also branches from the brachiocephalic. In sheep, only the brachiocephalic branches off the aortic arch.

e. The **superior vena cava** enters the **right atrium** on the right superior dorsal aspect, just behind the aorta. The superior vena cava drains the superior, or anterior in sheep/pig, body regions. The superior vena cava is the one closest to the aorta, and if not cut too short will point up. It has a thicker wall than the inferior vena cava.

f. The **inferior vena cava** with blood from inferior/posterior body regions enters the right atrium just above its line of union with the ventricle. The thin walls of the inferior vena cava often tear and collapse making it more difficult to locate. Through the vena cava you can easily probe the atrial interior and push the probe on into the right ventricle. The vena cavae are the major systemic veins returning blood to the right atrium.

g. Locate the **pulmonary veins** on the left dorsal side of the heart, superior and lateral to the inferior vena cava. They are entering the **left atrium**. There are four, but initially you may only find one, two or one large hole, if they were cut short. These veins are thin walled and are easy to tear. Probe these vessels. Remember that these are the only veins carrying oxygen rich blood.

10. Determine which side of the heart is the ventral side and which is the dorsal side. To the careful observer there is as much variation in the precise shape of the heart as there is the human face (due to the fact that our hearts have been preserved and placed in a bucket, many have taken on irregular shapes), but all share some common features. Remember the pulmonary trunk is always ventral and the inferior vena cava and pulmonary veins are dorsal.

11. Identify the chambers of the heart from the outside of the heart.

   a. At the top of the heart are two thin walled, irregularly shaped chambers, known as the **atria** (singular = atrium). The atria receive the venous blood returning to the heart. The earlike flap of each atrium on the heart surface is called an **auricle**. The auricles can expand during exercise permitting additional filling of the atria and in turn the ventricles. The superior vena cava and inferior vena cava are entering the right atrium. The pulmonary veins are entering the left atrium. Go no further until you are able to distinguish the right and left atria and their auricles.

   b. The main muscular mass of the heart is the **ventricles**. They are smooth and firm to the touch. The ventral side has a prominent oblique groove on the surface, the **anterior interventricular sulcus**. The groove runs from upper left, from the sheep's point of view, to lower right and marks the **interventricular septum**, the muscular wall which divides the **right and left ventricles**. Locate this groove now for it is a most important landmark. The upper end of the anterior interventricular sulcus points to the left auricle. In this sulcus lies the **anterior interventricular branch of the left coronary artery** but it is hidden by fat on the sheep/pig. The septum will be seen when the heart is opened.

   c. The **coronary sulcus** is the name for the groove between atria and ventricles which encircles the heart.

12. Now let's take a look at the inside of the heart. Locate the superior vena cava and using scissors cut its posterior wall into the right atrium. You want to be able to look down through the atrium to the atrioventricular valves and ventricle below. You may have to continue your cut downward through the horizontal fold of fat. Can you see the atrioventricular valve that separates the atrium from the ventricle?

13. Remove any clotted blood from the chambers as your dissection progresses, but do NOT leave that gunk in the sink. Leave on the paper towel to be put it in the disposal bag provided.

14. Continue this cut into the lateral wall of the right ventricle. The cut should be half way between the anterior interventricular sulcus and the posterior interventricular sulcus. The scissors should only cut through the lateral wall, and NOT into the septum. Spread the incision and look into the chamber. Inside, the endocardium is slick but there are deep

troughs in the wall. **Endocardium** is the slick membrane lining the heart chambers. Histologically, endocardium is identical to the epicaridum. The muscular wall separating the two ventricles is termed the interventricular septum. The irregular surface of ridges and folds of the myocardium inside the ventricles are termed the **trabeculae carneae**.

15. Locate the tough membranous flaps forming the **tricuspid** or **right atrioventricular valve**. The free moving edges of the valves are secured to **papillary muscles** on the ventricular walls by the thin but strong fibers, the **chordae tendineae**. The papillary muscles and chordae tendinae prevent the valves from being pushed into the atrium when the ventricle contracts increasing pressure on the blood. This arrangement of membranous valves and supporting cords minimizes resistance to blood flow within the heart yet effectively seals the atria when the ventricles contract. The blood has to go out the pulmonary trunk to the lungs because the tricuspid valve prevents its return to the atrium.

16. Look in the right atrium and identify the parallel ridges of muscle bundles in the anterior wall. They are termed **pectinate muscles** (*pecten* = comb). The pectinate muscles are only inside the atrium's flaplike extension known externally as the auricle. The term auricle does not apply to the chamber's interior. It is difficult to see the pectinate muscles on the heart models. They are best observed here.

17. Now look into the right ventricle and locate the **moderator band** of muscle which attaches the lateral wall to the septum. The moderator band is the route of the right atrioventricular bundle branch to the lateral wall of the right ventricle at the base of the lateral papillary muscle. The moderator band may also prevent over distention of the ventricle when filling. It is often not observed on the human heart and thus is not on the heart models. Its size is variable in the pig heart, varying from very wide to not present.

18. Blood flows from the right atrium into the right ventricle then out through the pulmonary trunk. Locate where the pulmonary trunk exits the right ventricle. Identify the **pulmonary semilunar valves** at the base of the trunk. Semilunar valves prevent flow of blood from arteries back into the ventricles, when the ventricle relaxes. Relaxation of the heart is called **diastole**.

19. Locate the most lateral of the pulmonary veins. Cut with a scissors vertically down through it into the left atrium. Continue the cut on downward through the left lateral ventricular wall to the apex, meeting the cut made in the right side of the heart. Cut through the interventricular septum. Open up the heart like you are opening the trunk of your car or your laptop and look in. From inside the atrium you should be able to locate with a probe the other one or two pulmonary veins you did not see from the surface. Pectinate muscles should also be found in the left atrium. Examine the **bicuspid or left atrioventricular valve** (also called the mitral valve) and its chordae tendinae and papillary muscles. The trabeculae carneae in the left ventricle are usually more prominent than on the right side of the heart. There is no moderator band in the left ventricle. Look behind the bicuspid valve on the posterior wall of the ventricle to see the aorta's exit. Look up there to see the bottom side of the **aortic semilunar valves**.

20. The **myocardium** is the cardiac muscle wall of the heart itself. **Most of the mass of the heart is left ventricular myocardium**! Determine the right and left sides of the heart. The left ventricle has thicker walls. The right ventricle is much thinner by comparison. The left ventricles heavier musculature is required to generate the high pressures required to drive the blood through the long systemic pathway where it encounters high resistance to flow. The lungs normally offer little resistance to flow so the right side does not develop as thick a muscle layer.

21. Using scissors, cut into the ventral wall of the pulmonary trunk, continuing the incision to its end. You only want to cut through the ventral wall, not into the dorsal. Spread the walls of the pulmonary trunk apart and cut towards the ventricle at its base. Locate the pulmonary semilunar valve at its connection with the right ventricle. Note the number of cusps, or flaps, comprising this valve.

22. Spray the heart inside and out with "Ward's Safe" and put it in a tagged plastic baggy to store for future study. Place the bagged heart in a labeled container under the hood until later use.

23. Clean your dissection tools by rinsing them with water in the sink. Throw away any unwanted dissected materials, paper towels, and gloves in the biohazard trash. Rinse your dissection tray and put away all dissection tools.

24. Identify and locate on the sheep/pig heart all structures in the table.

25. Complete the POST-LAB OBSERVATIONS section.

Sheep or Pig Heart Structures

Structure Name
apex of heart
base of heart
parietal pericardium
visceral pericardium = epicardium
endocardium
myocardium
pulmonary trunk
aorta
brachiocephalic artery
superior vena cava
inferior vena cava
left pulmonary veins
right pulmonary veins
right atrium
right auricle
left atrium
left auricle
right ventricle
left ventricle
anterior interventricular sulcus
interventricular septum
coronary sulcus
trabeculae carneae
tricuspid valve (= right atrioventricular valve = right AV valve)
papillary muscles
chordae tendineae
pectinate muscle (inside the walls of both auricles)
moderator band
bicuspid valve (= mitral valve = left atrioventricular valve = left AV valve)
pulmonary semilunar valves
aortic semilunar valve

III. MICROSCOPIC STRUCTURE OF CARDIAC MUSCLE

Introduction

The **myocardium** of the heart wall is made up of **cardiac muscle tissue**. Cardiac muscle cells have a single nucleus and are striated. This pattern of alternating light and dark bands is due to the precise overlapping and non-overlapping of protein filaments within each muscle cell. The darker bands are the site where the ends of thousands of filaments overlap. In the heart, muscle fibers course in many directions. Cardiac muscle cells also branch and the branches terminate in blunt ends. The ends of each cell are tightly joined to the ends of other cells forming **intercalated discs**. These tight junctions provide for efficient intercellular communication. Cardiac muscle cells are also autorhythmic; they can spontaneously generate action potentials and contract independently of nervous stimulation.

PROCEDURE

1. Retrieve your microscope from the microscope cabinet.

2. Obtain the slide **"Muscle, heart intercalated disks, ls"** from a slide box. The cardiac muscle slides may be stained with the usual dyes and appear pink to purple, but some are stained blue.

3. Focus using the scanning 5X objective. Turn to the 10X objective to scan the section and locate an area where the fibers can be viewed from the side. The muscle cells are in close proximity with only small amounts of connective tissue connecting neighboring cells. As the specimen was prepared, tears occurred producing the clear areas.

4. Under 40X you should be able to distinguish the oval nucleus. Each cell has only one nucleus. A definite pattern of **striations** can be seen. You may need to rotate your fine focusing knob back and forth a bit to see the striations. The intercalated discs are seen as the occasional dark line perpendicular to the fiber's length.

5. Draw a section of cardiac muscle in the POST-LAB OBSERVATIONS section.

6. Clean your microscope, lock the scanning objective in place, wind the cord loosely around one eyepiece, put on its dust cover, and return the microscope to the proper location is the microscope cabinet.

Cardiac Muscle Structures

Structure Name
myocardium
cardiac muscle tissue
intercalated discs
nucleus
striations

Heart 2- 14

PRE-LAB QUESTIONS　　　　　　　**Name** _____

Define or describe the following structures:

A. Moderator Band

B. Visceral pericardium

C. Chordae tendinae

D. Auricle

E. Ligamentum arteriosum

From the history: What structure did Galen say had "pores"? _____

F. Figure 5. Anterior, interior view of the human heart. Using a pencil label structures indicated. Check your answers by comparing your labels to the textbook. You are encouraged to cover your answers and repeat the labeling outside of lab time. Exams use the models, not these drawings.

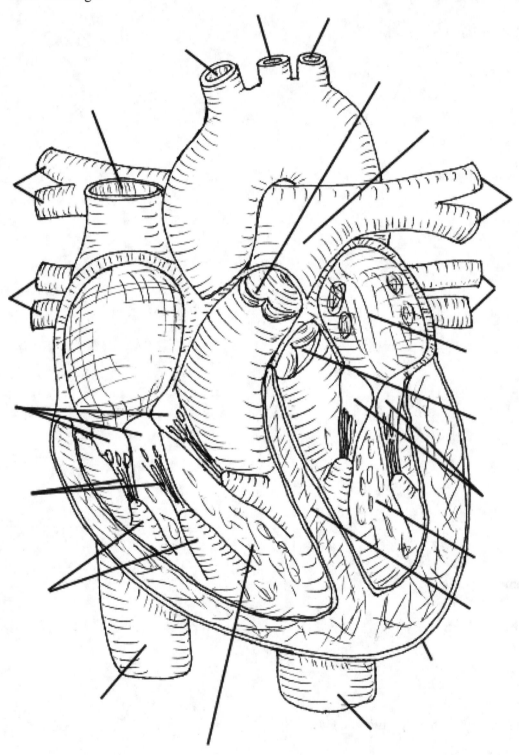

POST-LAB OBSERVATIONS

I. HUMAN HEART ANATOMY - HEART MODELS

A. Figure 6. Anterior view of the human heart. This drawing is intended as a self test, to be labeled AFTER you have studied the models and the textbook. Using a pencil label structures indicated. Check your answers by comparing your labels to the textbook. You are encouraged to cover your answers and repeat the self-test outside of lab time. Exams use the models, not these drawings.

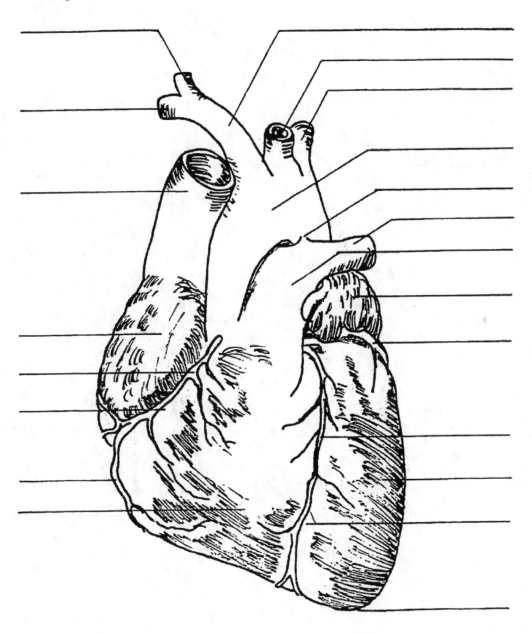

B. Figure 7. Posterior view of the human heart. This drawing is intended as a self test, to be labeled AFTER you have studied the models and the textbook. Using a pencil label structures indicated. Check your answers by comparing your labels to the textbook. You are encouraged to cover your answers and repeat the self-test outside of lab time. Exams use the models, not these drawings.

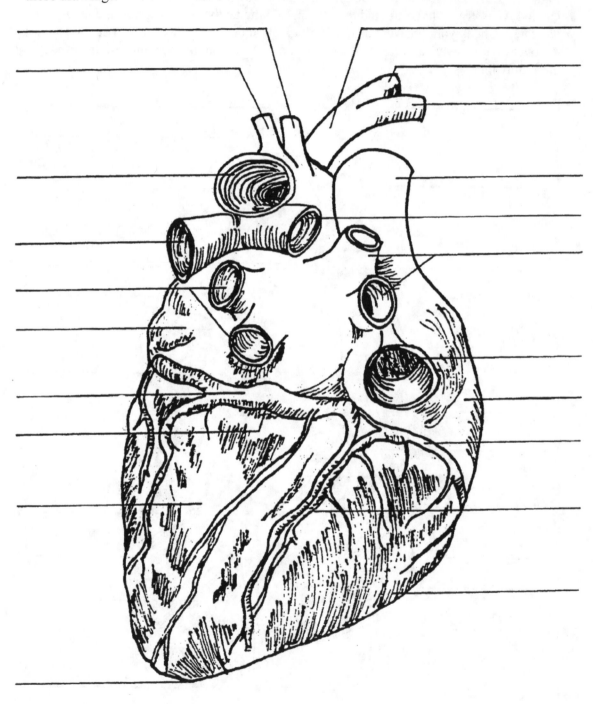

C. Figure 8. Superior view of heart valves after great vessels and atria have been dissected away. Label valves and vessels as indicated.

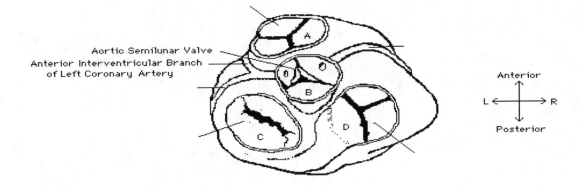

1. What heart chamber is inferior to A on the diagram? _____

2. What heart chamber is inferior to B on the diagram? _____

3. What heart chamber is superior to C on the diagram? _____

4. What heart chamber is superior to D on the diagram? _____

II. SHEEP OR PIG HEART ANATOMY

A. Examine the right and left atrioventricular valves of the sheep heart. Describe any differences in the valve cusps, chordae tendineae, and papillary muscles. (Which are larger?)

B. The ventricles contract simultaneously. Do you think the right ventricle can pump the same volume of blood as the left ventricle at each beat?

How do you know?

C. Notice the difference in thickness of the myocardium of the right and left ventricles. There is resistance to blood flow through the peripheral blood vessels. The heart pumps blood against this resistance. Muscles become stronger and larger as they work against a resistance.

Which ventricle has had to work the hardest?

Is peripheral resistance greatest in the systemic or pulmonary circulation pathway?

D. Figure 9. Ventral view of the sheep heart. After you have studied the sheep heart, label this drawing as a self-test using a pencil. Check your answers by comparing your labels to Figure 2. You are encouraged to cover your answers and repeat the self-test outside of lab time. Exams use the sheep heart and models, not these drawings.

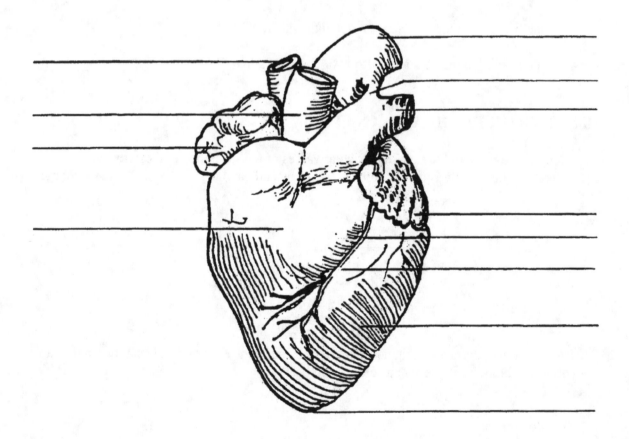

BLOOD AND LYMPH VESSELS

HISTORY

As the arteries are empty after death, Aristotle and others thought they carried air. In fact, the name "artery" means air channel. Galen did acknowledge that arteries carried blood. However, blood was given its "natural spirit" in the liver from the "chyle" of the digestive tract and from there it flowed to the tissues through the veins and then back to the liver via the same veins.

The Englishman William Harvey, one of the great pioneers of physiology, began his work in the early 1600s at the Royal College of Physicians in London. Using animals, he showed that the valves of the heart promote one way flow of blood. Using a classic demonstration of the venous valves on the arm of a living subject, he showed that the veins also have valves that promote one way flow of blood. This rejected the "ebb and flow" idea long held by followers of Galen. He also determined quantitatively that the blood pumped in an hour is equivalent to three times the weight of the average man. It had to travel in a circle. This idea of the circulation of the blood was put forth in his epic work *De Motu Cordis* in 1628. The true nature of the circle would not be completed until 40 years later with the discovery of the microscopic capillaries by Marcello Malpighi.

OBJECTIVES

1. To list the major arteries and veins serving each body region.
2. To compare the microscopic structure of arteries and veins.
3. To observe the flow of blood in vessels of a living goldfish tail.
4. To observe the valves in lymph vessels.
5. To observe the function of veins.

I. MAJOR SYSTEMIC ARTERIES AND VEINS

Introduction

Arteries carry blood away from the heart. The large arteries divide into smaller and smaller branches called **arterioles** eventually draining into networks of **capillaries** which permeate every part of the body. The capillary walls are only one thin cell thick and are the site of exchange between the blood and the cells of all tissues. Small vessels called **venules** unite to become **veins** which collect the blood from the tissues and carry it toward the heart. Thus, the blood is always contained within these vessels from the time it leaves the heart until it returns. Some of the **plasma**, the liquid part of the blood without dissolved proteins, may leave the capillaries to bathe the cells. Most of this fluid returns to the capillaries. Any remaining fluid is picked up by another system of very permeable vessels, the **lymphatic system**, and returned to the veins. This system has no pump (besides the external action of skeletal muscles) and carries the fluid in only one direction, from the body tissues toward the heart.

The arteries, veins and nerves serving a region or organ usually run alongside one another in a bundle. Think of it as a **triad**, AVN. The components of a triad usually share a common name. In the thigh the femoral artery, femoral vein and femoral nerve form a triad. Along the radius is the radial artery, vein and nerve. The nomenclature is not always this simple, the common carotid artery, internal jugular vein and vagus nerve run together in the neck. Triads do not run through muscles and organs but lie in the connective tissue in between. The pattern of artery, vein and nerve branching and their arrangement follows a logical design with a sound embryological basis.

The larger the artery the deeper it is located in the trunk or limb. Arteries tend to run on the flexor rather than the extensor side of a limb. The superficial veins on the extensor surface of our limbs are not part of a triad, they lack accompanying large arteries and nerves.

The study of blood vessels is **angiology**. **Angiography** is the study and mapping of vessels, usually using radiation and an injected radio-opaque material.

Arteries

Humans have three branches off the **aortic arch**: 1) the **brachiocephalic artery**, which branches into the **right subclavian artery** and **right common carotid artery**, 2) the **left common carotid artery** and 3) the **left subclavian artery**. You should remember these from your study of the heart. In the pig and cat only two branches, the brachiocephalic and left subclavian, come off the aorta because the left common carotid branches from the brachiocephalic. In sheep both carotids and both subclavians arise from the brachiocephalic, so it is the only branch off the aortic arch. The subclavian arteries become the **axillary arteries** when they pass from behind the first rib. The name changes to brachial artery when the vessel passes the lower margin of the Teres major. The brachial artery, which is the one used in obtaining blood pressure, divides into the **radial** and **ulnar** arteries in front of the elbow.

The common carotids branch into the **internal and external carotids** near the angle of the jaw. The external carotids will supply blood to structures outside of the skull and the internal carotids supply the structures inside the skull, such as the brain. Under the brain, located near the sella turcica is the **Circle of Willis.** The Circle of Willis is a ring of interconnected arteries that provides collateral circulation to the brain. The circle of Willis is receiving blood from both the **internal carotids** and the **vertebral arteries**.

After the aortic arch the aorta is called the descending aorta. In the chest it is called the **thoracic aorta** and after passing through the diaphragm it is called the **abdominal aorta**. In the thorax small **intercostal arteries** branch off to supply the chest wall. The first branch off the abdominal aorta below the diaphragm is the **celiac trunk**. The celiac trunk (artery) divides into three vessels: 1) the **hepatic artery** to the liver, 2) the **gastric artery** to the stomach, and 3) the **splenic artery** to the spleen. The next branch off the abdominal aorta is the **superior mesenteric artery** which supplies the intestine and has branches to the stomach and pancreas as well. The **renal arteries** branch off the abdominal aorta next and supply the kidneys. These carry anywhere from 1/7 to 1/4 of your total cardiac output! There are additional branches from the aorta to the digestive tract, body wall, bladder and reproductive organs. For example the **lumbar** arteries supply the lumbar region, while the **inferior mesenteric artery** branches to the colon and rectum.

The aorta ends in the pelvis where it divides into the **common iliac arteries**. The **internal iliac arteries** branch off to supply the organs in the pelvic cavity and nearby muscles. The **external iliac arteries** exit the pelvis though the femoral ring below the inguinal ligament.

Once in the thigh the external iliac arteries become the **femoral arteries**. Behind the knee the artery becomes the **popliteal artery** which branches into the **anterior and posterior tibial arteries**. The anterior tibial artery will eventually lead to the **dorsalis pedis artery** located on the top of your foot.

Veins

Remember that most of the veins parallel the arteries and return blood to the heart. In the upper extremity you will find the **radial vein** in the lateral forearm and the **ulnar vein** in the medial forearm. These two veins will flow into the deep vein of the arm, the **brachial vein**. There are some superficial veins on the anterior surface of the upper extremity. The **basilic vein** runs along the medial side of the arm and forearm. The **cephalic vein** runs along the lateral side of the upper extremity. Both can be used to obtain blood by venous puncture. An additional vein, the **median cubital** runs across the inside of the elbow and drains into the basilic vein. The median cubital is the most commonly used vein to obtain blood by venous puncture. The brachial and basilic veins unite to form the **axillary vein**. The cephalic joins the axillary to form the **subclavian vein** as they enter the chest wall.

The **external jugular vein** descends the side of the neck superficial to the sternocleidomastoid muscle carrying blood from the scalp and face before going deep to join the subclavian vein in the chest. The external jugular vein is the prominent neck vein noticed in some slender or muscular folks. (Blow with your mouth closed to make it more visible.) Deep in the neck alongside the carotid arteries are the larger **internal jugular veins** draining the brain, parts of the face and neck. The internal jugulars join the subclavian veins in the base of the neck to form the **brachiocephalic vein**s which then unite behind the sternum to form the **superior vena cava**. Note that there are two braciocephalic veins, but only one brachiocephalic artery!

Veins that drain the thoracic cavity join to form the **azygos vein**. The **azygos vein** runs up the right side of the thoracic vertebral column and enters into the posterior superior vena cava right before it enters the right atrium.

In the legs there are **anterior and posterior tibial veins** which joins to become the **popliteal** and then **femoral vein**. The long vein on the medial aspect of the leg and thigh is the **great saphenous vein**. It joins the femoral vein in the groin. The saphenous vein may become varicose. At its distal end it is anterior to the medial malleolus. It is often used for the intravenous administration of fluids and was once commonly used as the source for vessel material grafted in coronary bypass surgery. Blood from the femoral veins flows into the **external iliac veins**. The **internal iliac veins** join with the external iliac veins to form the **common iliac veins**. These unite to form the **inferior vena cava**. The inferior vena cava picks up blood from other veins such as the **lumbar veins** and **renal veins** and takes blood from all the lower extremities back to the heart.

Fetal circulation is a subject covered in lecture and the text, but will not be studied in lab.

Procedure

1. Locate all of the arteries and veins in the tables on any available model that shows them well. Structures grayed out in the table are not shown on that model.

Keys for Blood Vessels

Arteries	Flat Guy	½ Size Standing Man	¾ Torso
Pulmonary Trunk (blue)	48	152	149
Pulmonary Arteries (blue)	46 or 47		
Aortic Arch	20	149	151
Brachiocephalic	16a		157
Vertebral	14		
Right Common Carotid	18		
Right Subclavian	16		
Left Common Carotid	19	47	92
External Carotid	18a		93
Internal Carotid			94
Left Subclavian	26		159
Axillary	21		110
Brachial	24		
Radial	32		
Ulnar	29		
Thoracic Aorta		150	150
Abdominal Aorta	68	159	102
Celiac trunk	61a	155	103
Hepatic	61	194	193
Gastric	67		
Splenic	66		
Superior Mesenteric	65	156	104
Renal	64		
Inferior Mesenteric	69	158	105
Common Iliac	72	160	107
Internal Iliac (red)	75		108
External Iliac	73	162	
Femoral	78		111
Popliteal			
Anterior Tibial			
Posterior Tibial			

Vessels 3 - 4

Keys for Blood Vessels

Veins	Flat Guy	½ Size Standing Man	¾ Torso
Pulmonary veins (red)	46 or 47	153	146
Superior Vena Cava	17	148	144
Azygos			113
Brachiocephalic	17a (there are actually two of these but the other is not shown well)		
Internal Jugular	10	43	112
External Jugular			
Right Subclavian	16		
Left Subclavian		44	161
Axillary			160
Cephalic	22		
Basilic	27		
Brachial			
Median Cubital			
Inferior Vena Cava	63	151	115 & 145
Renal	64		
Common Iliac	72	163	116
Internal Iliac (blue)	75		
External Iliac	73	164	
Femoral	Cut and not labeled		117
Great Saphenous	99		

2. Palpitate a pulse in the:
   a. brachial artery along the medial surface of the humerus, between the biceps brachii and triceps brachii near the armpit
   b. radial and ulnar arteries at your wrist
   c. common carotid artery alongside your trachea
   d. external carotid artery by the angle of the jaw
   e. facial artery alongside the jaw behind the angle of the mouth, and also in the groove between the cheek and nose
   f. temporal artery against the temple in front of your ear
   g. femoral in the groin area midway between the anterior superior iliac spine and pubis
   h. popliteal behind the knee
   i. posterior tibial behind the medial malleolus
   j. dorsalis pedis arteries over the instep of your foot

3. Look at the model of the Circle of Willis.

4. Complete the exercises in the POST-LAB OBSERVATIONS section.

II. MICROSCOPIC STRUCTURE OF THE BLOOD VESSELS

Introduction

The walls of blood vessels, except capillaries consist of three coats or tunics around a hollow **lumen** through which the blood flows. The inner coat is the **tunica interna**, a single thin layer of **simple squamous epithelium** or **endothelium**. The endothelium of the arteries continues into the capillaries, veins and on into the heart as the **endocardium**. It is the only layer present in the microscopic capillaries. The cells are smooth and fit close together providing low resistance to blood flow. Just below the epithelium, yet a part of the tunica interna, is the **internal elastic membrane**. The middle coat is the **tunica media** which is the thickest layer in an artery. It consists of layers of smooth muscle fibers with elastic fibers in between the muscle cells. The smooth muscle is under the control of the sympathetic division of the autonomic nervous system. Depending on location, sympathetic activity may stimulate the muscle to contract reducing lumen diameter, **vasoconstriction**, increasing peripheral resistance and blood pressure. Elsewhere, sympathetic stimulation can inhibit contraction and dilates vessels, **vasodilation**. There is increasing evidence that vessels are capable of detecting and responding directly to local conditions, thus self-regulating blood flow. The **tunica externa** is the outermost coat. It is composed primarily of elastic and collagenous fibers and is usually described as elastic connective tissue. This layer grades into areolar connective tissue and irregular dense fibrous connective tissue which wraps the triads.

Comparing an artery to a vein of similar external diameter we would see two obvious differences. The artery has much thicker walls and a smaller lumen. Examine your textbook's illustrations of an artery and vein. The artery needs stronger walls because it is subjected to much higher pressures. When the ventricles contract, blood is forced into the arteries which expand with the increased volume of blood. The elastic recoil of the arteries after this initial stretching forces the blood onward into more distant vessels. The smooth muscle layers are primarily responsible for the contraction of an artery. The wave of distension which passes along an artery with each heart beat is termed a **pulse**. The large arteries are very elastic and commonly experience pressure fluctuations of 40 mm Hg or more. As they divide into smaller and smaller branches the pressure surges tend to even out until in the capillaries there is no fluctuating pressure, just a smooth uniform flow. Beyond the capillaries, the veins are not subjected to high fluctuating pressures. See the illustration, present in most textbooks, showing the pressure in the various types of vessels.

Notice on the graph that the pressure in the veins is very low and realize that blood in the veins is generally flowing uphill against gravity. Valves, particularly in the larger veins, help prevent the backflow of blood and so help it return. There are many superficial or cutaneous veins near the surface but most of the blood is returned to the heart by the deep veins lying alongside arteries. Both deep and surface veins are easily compressed due to their thin walls. The pressure of skeletal muscle action on the thin walls also helps return venous blood. Blood is also aided in its return by the low pressure in the chest upon inspiration.

Procedures

1. Obtain your microscope and set it up at your station. Start your study of arteries and veins with the slide labeled "**Artery, vein, & nerve, c.s.**".

2. Under scanning, locate the triad of artery, vein and nerve. This cross section is through a smaller midsize artery and you will see a vein and two or more associated nerves. Both the artery and vein may contain blood within their lumen. The artery has the thicker walls. Switch to 10X and determine that there are actually three layers as previously described. Observe the artery first.

3. Turn to 40X and move to the tunica interna of the artery. It has a wavy or convoluted appearance. The walls recoiled when they were cut. An artery filled with blood under pressure would have its lining stretched out smooth. You should be able to locate the nuclei of the simple squamous epithelium forming the endothelium because they bulge into the lumen. Just below the endothelium is a thin homogenous pink layer, the internal elastic membrane. It is this elastic membrane that recoiled into folds when the blood drained out.

4. The tunica media of the artery is the thick layer below. The high density of nuclei of smooth muscle cells gives this layer a slight purplish hue. Examine a few nuclei and note their elongate shape.

5. Outside the tunica media there is a change to more of a pink color. This layer is the tunica externa of the artery. Nuclei are less abundant and are more rounded. These are primarily the nuclei of **fibroblasts**. If there are fibroblasts you know there must be fibers. You can find the wavy purple elastic fibers. Much of the pinkish/orange cast in this layer is due to the presence of collagenous fibers. This layer has basically a protective function and gives the artery strength so as not to be damaged by the high pressure.

6. Nearby the artery, perhaps even compressed against it, you will find a vein. The lumen may contain clotted blood. The endothelium is the same as in an artery. But in the vein you will not see the internal elastic membrane obvious in the artery. Both the tunica media and tunica externa are much thinner in comparison with the artery. Thus the vein's wall lacks the structural rigidity of an artery and readily collapses. This gives veins the low pressure necessary to help blood return to the venous end of the capillary bed.

7. Complete the drawings of the artery, vein and nerve in the POST-LAB OBSERVATIONS.

Blood Vessel Structures

Structure Name
artery
vein
nerve
tunica interna
simple squamous epithelium
internal elastic membrane
tunica media
smooth muscle
tunica externa
fibroblasts
collagen fibers

III. MICROSCOPIC STRUCTURE OF LIVING VESSELS

Introduction

The walls of capillaries are only one thin cell thick, the tunica interna, and they are transparent. This exceptional thinness facilitates exchanges between the blood and surrounding tissues. Capillaries permeate every part of the body. Materials diffuse into and out of the blood through the capillary wall from nearby cells. The forces of capillary dynamics are described in your textbook.

Procedures

1. Turn the mechanical stage of your microscope out of the way. Place a microscope slide over the opening in the stage.

2. Obtain a goldfish from the aquarium and wrap it with a layer of dripping wet cotton leaving the mouth and tail exposed. Then wrap the fish with a strip of aluminum foil in a manner that will prevent the water from getting on the microscope.

3. Place the fish on the stage and gently spread the tail over the slide covered opening in the stage.

4. Observe under low power magnification the blood flow through the arterioles, capillaries, and venules.

5. Notice the erythrocytes moving single file through the capillaries.

6. Complete your observation within 5 minutes and record your observations in the POST-LAB OBSERVATION section. Return your fish to the water!!

IV. MICROSCOPIC STRUCTURE OF LYMPH VESSELS

Introduction

Lymph capillaries are blind end vessels with very permeable walls. Pores occur between adjacent cells. The simple squamous epithelial cells are structured around a pore as one way valves, permitting fluids to easily enter the lymph vessel but the exit is restricted. Fluids which escape the cardiovascular system's capillaries are picked up by the lymph capillaries. Lymph capillaries are drained by the **lymphatics**, a system of interconnected vessels. Lymphatics often parallel veins and are similar in structure, except lymphatics have more valves and thinner walls.

Procedures

1. Obtain the slide "**Lymphatic vessel & valve**" and examine it under low power. These sections are longitudinal.

2. Draw a lymph vessel and valve in the POST-LAB OBSERVATION section. Valves in veins are similar in design and performance but are more massive.

Lymphatic Vessel Structures

Structure Name
lymphatic vessel
valve

V. DEMONSTRATION OF VENOUS VALVES

Introduction

In the early 1600s, William Harvey preformed this same demonstration to illustrate the function of the valves within the veins. In a living subject, he showed that the veins have valves that promote one way flow of blood.

Procedures

1. Hang one of your hands by your side to allow the veins to become distended. Tensing the muscles in the forearm may help make the veins more prominent.

2. With your other hand press the middle finger and thumb firmly against one of the distended veins.

3. Now move the thumb up the forearm pushing blood up the vein.

4. Release the thumb and blood will only flow down to a point where a valve blocks flow.

5. Release the finger and blood quickly fills the collapsed vein.

PRE-LAB QUESTIONS   Name _____

I. MAJOR SYSTEMIC ARTERIES AND VEINS

A. Arrange the terms **in a circle** in order of flow: venule, capillary, vein, artery, heart, arteriole.

B. What three things often run in a *triad*?

_____

_____

_____

C. List five arteries where it is possible to palpate a pulse.

_____

_____

_____

_____

_____

D. Supply the name of the artery or vein for each question.

_____ artery supplying the liver

_____ vein draining the kidney

_____ formed when the subclavian and jugular veins unite

_____ right and left terminal branches of the abdominal aorta

_____ artery along the humerus used to obtain blood pressure

_____ arteries that can be used for pulse at the wrist

_____ the first branch off the aorta below the diaphragm

_____ arteries supplying the heart

_____ name the first branch off the aortic arch

_____ the first two branches off the aorta

_____

_____ the vein under the clavicle

_____ artery supplying most of the small intestine

_____ the major vein inferior to the heart

_____ a superficial vein which may become varicose

_____ the vein entering the heart carrying oxygenated blood

E. List the names of the 3 branches of the celiac trunk.

_____

_____

_____

F. List two veins in the arm commonly used for drawing blood.

_____

_____

G. List the two main arteries in the neck which supply the Circle of Willis of the brain.

_____

_____

Vessels 3 - 12

H. Label all of the arteries on the following diagram.

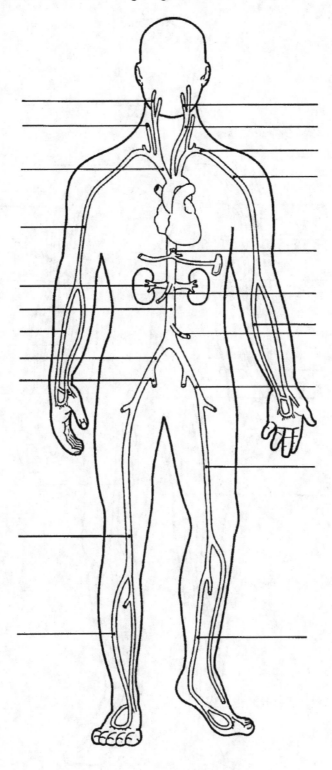

Figure 11–8 Arteries

I. Label all of the veins on the following diagram.

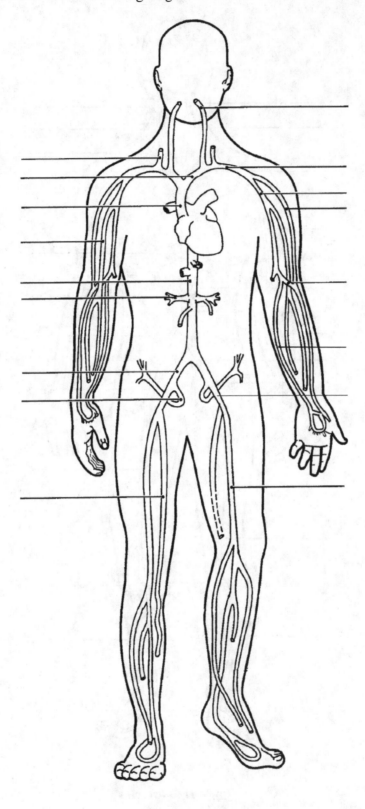

Figure 11-7 Veins

II. MICROSCOPIC STRUCTURE OF THE BLOOD VESSELS

A. Matching:

    a. tunica interna   b. tunica media   c. tunica externa

_____ only coat (tunic) present in capillaries
_____ the outermost supporting, protective coat of arteries and veins
_____ consists primarily of smooth muscle fibers
_____ continues through all blood vessels and into the lining of the heart
_____ this layer is thickest in arteries
_____ includes the internal elastic membrane
_____ comprised only of simple squamous epithelial tissue
_____ the coat primarily responsible for vasoconstriction

III. MICROSCOPIC STRUCTURE OF LIVING VESSELS

A. What is the maximum amount of time you should have the goldfish out of the water when observing the flow of blood though the capillaries of the tail?

IV. MICROSCOPIC STRUCTURE OF LYMPH VESSELS

A. How are lymph vessels different from blood vessels?

V. DEMONSTRATION OF VENOUS VALVES

A. Why are valves present in veins, but not in arteries?

From the History: What did William Harvey prove in his demonstration of venous valves?

POST-LAB OBSERVATIONS

I. MAJOR SYSTEMIC ARTERIES AND VEINS

A. Sketch and label the following arteries of the head, neck, thoracic and abdominal cavity.
Pulmonary Trunk, Pulmonary Arteries, Aortic Arch, Thoracic Aorta, Abdominal Aorta,
Brachiocephalic, Left Common Carotid, Right Common Carotid, External Carotid, Internal
Carotid, Left Subclavian, Right Subclavian, Vertebral, Celiac trunk, Hepatic, Gastric,
Splenic, Superior Mesenteric, Inferior Mesenteric, Renal, and Common Iliac.

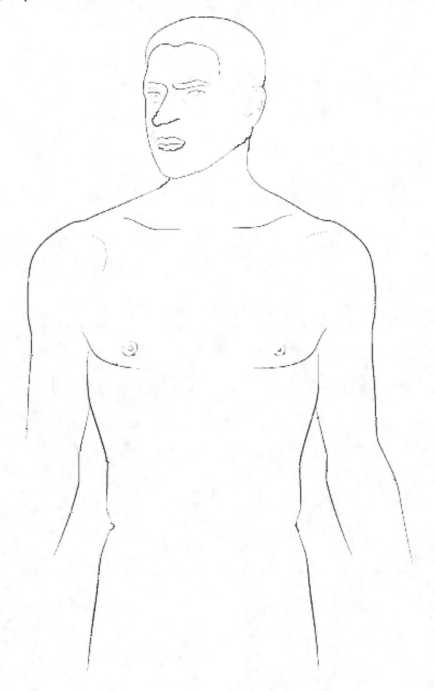

B. Sketch and label the following the veins of the head, neck, thoracic and abdominal cavity. Pulmonary, Superior Vena Cava, Azygos, Brachiocephalic, Internal Jugular, External Jugular, Right Subclavian, Left Subclavian, Inferior Vena Cava, Renal, and Common Iliac

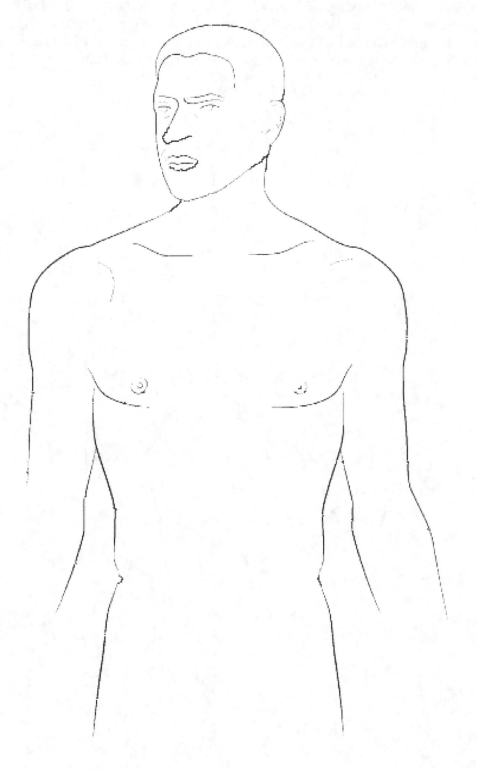

C. Sketch and label the following the arteries of the thoracic cavity and upper extremity.
   Right Subclavian, Axillary, Brachial, Radial, and Ulnar

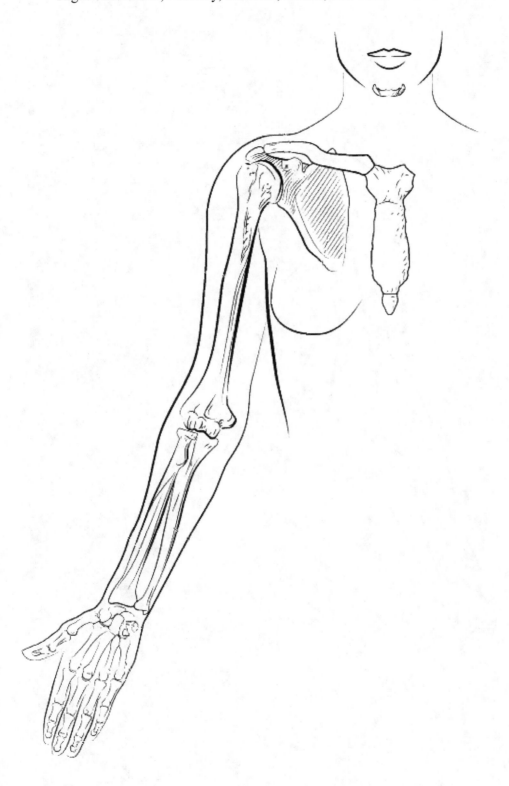

D. Sketch and label the following the veins of the thoracic cavity and upper extremity. Right Subclavian, Axillary, Cephalic, Basilic, Brachial, and Median Cubital

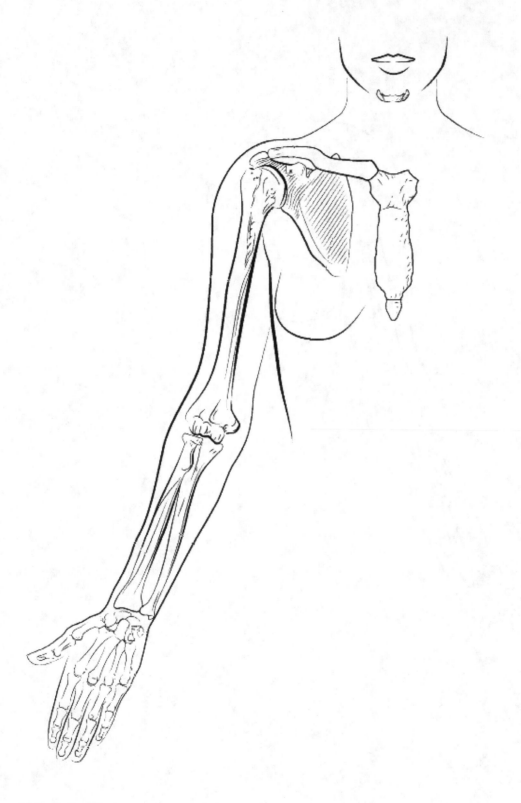

E. Sketch and label the following the arteries of the pelvic region and lower extremity. Abdominal Aorta, Common Iliac, Internal Iliac, External Iliac, Femoral, Popliteal, Anterior Tibial, and Posterior Tibial

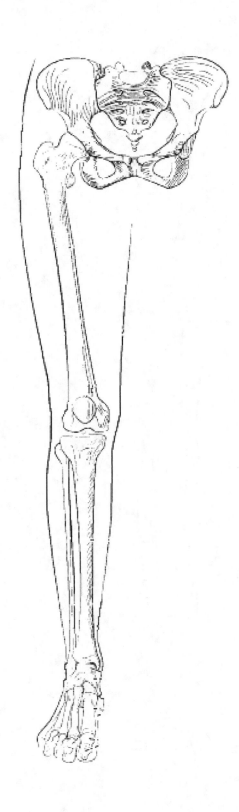

F. Sketch and label the following the veins of the pelvic region and lower extremity. Inferior Vena Cava, Common Iliac, Internal Iliac, External Iliac, Femoral and Great Saphenous

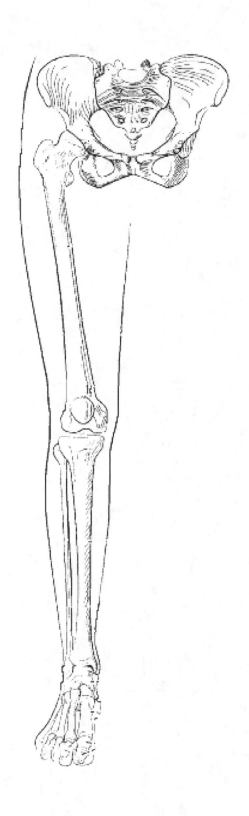

ELECTROCARDIOGRAM, HEART SOUNDS, and BLOOD PRESSURE

HISTORY

In 1790, Luigi Galvani made a dead frog's legs dance by electrical stimulation, thus showing that skeletal muscle movement was related to electricity. In 1855, two German scientists determined that the beating of the heart was also due to electrical stimuli. In 1901, another German, Dr. Willem Einthoven, invented the electrocardiograph machine and first observed the waves he named P, QRS, and T. The term "EKG" is often used rather than ECG to honor the German spelling.

OBJECTIVES

1. To record an electrocardiogram using each of the three standard lead positions, I, II, and III.
2. To record an electrocardiogram using each of the three augmented leads, AVR, AVL and AVF.
3. To compare the EKGs from Leads I, II and III with one another.
4. To identify the P, QRS and T waves on an EKG.
5. To calculate the heart rate from an EKG.
6. To measure the amplitude of the P, QRS and T waves on Lead II and convert to voltage estimates.
7. To measure the duration in time of the P, QRS and T waves on Lead II and convert to time.
8. To measure the P-Q (=P-R) interval, Q-T interval and S-T interval and S-T segment on Lead II and convert to time.
9. To identify typical heart sounds.
10. To use a sphygmomanometer to measure blood pressure.

I. ELECTROCARDIOGRAM

Introduction

Many cells exhibit a difference in electrical charge between the inside and outside of their cell membrane. This is called the **resting membrane potential**. This potential is particularly important to nerve and muscle cells. The resting potential is due to an unequal distribution of ions across the membrane. The sodium/potassium pumps continually expend energy moving these ions across the cell membrane. The positively charged sodium is now in excess outside the cell. Positively charged potassium is now in excess inside the cell. The cell is now said to be **polarized**. Potassium easily diffuses outward and this positive potassium efflux, along with a concentration of negative proteins inside the cell keeps the outside of the cell membrane positive and the inside of the cell membrane negative.

When these cells are sufficiently stimulated, the potential changes due to increased membrane permeability to sodium. The rapid diffusion of positive sodium ions through the membrane into the cell changes the electric field as the inside of the cell membrane is now positive relative to the outside. The cell is now said to be **depolarized** and an **action potential** develops signaling cell activity. This depolarization spreads as a wave through the cell, from cell to cell, and eventually throughout the heart and then through the body to the surface.

It is possible to record at the body surface signals representing the changing electric field resulting from the combined action potentials of many cells. Recording electrodes are placed in contact with the skin. The potentials received at the electrodes are amplified and used to drive a recording pen over moving paper. The greater the electrical activity, the more the pen moves. The potentials can also be displayed on an oscilloscope screen, such as the heart monitors used in clinics.

The depolarization of the myocardium, the change of cell membrane interiors from a negative to a positive charge, spreads from cell to cell through the intercalated discs between the cardiac muscle cells. Visualize this as a flow of positive charges. When positive charges flow toward a positive electrode they cause a positive deflection, and the pen moves up. If + charges are flowing toward a negative or away from a positive electrode the pen moves down. If the heart is normal, most of the leads will have the flow of electricity toward the positive recording electrode and thus an upward sweep of the pen.

We can measure the electrical signaling of the electrically active tissues in the body. If these signals originate from the brain we call the recording an **electroencephalogram or EEG**, from skeletal muscles an **electromyogram, EMG**, and if from the heart muscle an **electocardiogram, ECG**, (or **EKG**, from the historic German spelling "electrokardiogram"). Fortunately, these signals are of different frequencies so it was possible to design recording instruments capable of tuning in the desired organ. Muscle and heart signals are quite similar and, as you will see, contractions of skeletal muscles produce significant disturbances in an EKG.

Electrocardiograms have a repeating pattern of three waves called the P, QRS complex and T wave. Each normal heart beat produces these three waves. To learn what the normal observed electrocardiogram wave forms represent, and what the abnormal wave forms indicate in terms of actual heart function has required decades of research.

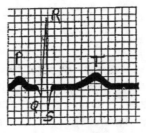

Figure 1. Normal Electrocardiogram labeled with its wave forms.

Each heart cycle will produce the three distinct waves in a typical EKG. The **P wave** is a small upward deflection resulting from the **depolarization of the atria**. This wave of depolarization was initiated by the pacemaker cells in the **sinoatrial (SA) node**. The P wave precedes the contraction of the atria. The electrical signal will pass through all of the myocardial cells of the atria to the **atrioventricular node**, or **AV node**. Usually less than 0.2 seconds after the P wave begins and the signal has passed though the AV node, the QRS wave begins. The **QRS complex** begins as a short downward deflection, Q, followed by a sharp upward wave, R, ending in a downward deflection, S, below the base line. The QRS complex corresponds to the **depolarization of the ventricles**. The AV node fired off an impulse down the **AV bundle (Bundle of His)** to the **Purkinje fibers** and on through the ventricular myocardium producing ventricular depolarization. This pathway is necessary so that the AV node can delay the signal in order for the ventricles to fill. Passage of the signal down the AV bundle and up through the Purkinje fibers allows the heart to depolarize from the apex upward. The QRS precedes the contraction of the ventricles. The third wave of the EKG is the small dome shaped **T wave** which results from the electrical **repolarization of the ventricles**. Repolarization of the ventricles precedes the relaxation of the ventricles. Repolarization of the atria normally occurs at the same time the ventricles are depolarizing. Thus the QRS wave masks this event.

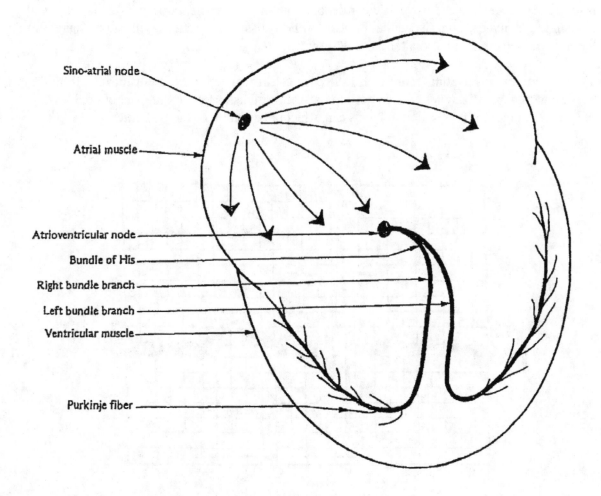

Figure 2. Electrical Conduction System of the Heart.

Remember the SA node is located in the right atrium and the heart is normally lying in the thoracic cavity with the apex tipped toward the left. In general, the flow of positive charges though the bulk of the heart is in a superior to inferior and right to left direction.

The **duration** of a wave reflects the **time** it takes to depolarize or repolarize that part of the heart. Durations are measured from the beginning or end of one wave to the beginning or end of another wave. The durations are called either **intervals** or **segments**. An interval includes a wave, a segment does not. (See Figure 3) Measurements outside of the normal range can reflect damage to that area.

The **P-Q (P-R) interval** is the time between the beginning of the P wave and the beginning of the QRS wave. This is the time required for the depolarization wave to spread across the atria, for the AV node to fire and depolarization to begin to spread over the ventricles. The normal P-Q (P-R) interval is less than 0.2 sec. Scarring or inflammation of the conducting tissues (heart block) slows down impulse travel resulting in an increase in this interval. As the heart rate increases during exercise, the P-Q (P-R) interval shortens.

The **S-T segment** begins at the end of the S wave and ends at the beginning of the T wave. This is the time between the end of ventricular depolarization and ventricular repolarization. Lack of oxygen to the myocardium (ischemia) or death of heart tissue (infarction) will cause changes in the S-T segment and will also alter the **S-T interval**.

The **Q-T interval** is the time required for the entire electrical activity of the ventricle, from the beginning to depolarization to the end of repolarization. This usually requires about 0.34 seconds. Changes in blood calcium levels can affect the duration of the Q-T interval.

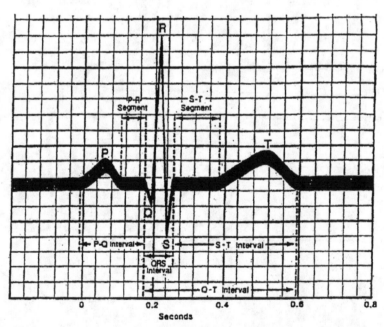

Figure 3. Normal electrocardiogram enlarged to show how various wave segments are measured.

(From: Tortora & Anagnostakos, 1990. Principles of Anatomy and Physiology, Harper & Row)

Assuming the conductivity of the human body is rather constant, measuring the **amplitude** of the P, QRS and T waves gives an indication of the strength of the current being generated when the heart depolarizes and repolarizes. The strength of the current and thus the amplitude of the wave reflects the **mass** of the myocardium that is sensed. Many years of research has determined what the normal range of amplitude for each wave is.

Enlargement of the P wave outside the normal range indicates enlargement of the atria. Atria enlarge when they encounter increased resistance upon contraction, such as when the AV valves are stenotic (narrowed). The Q wave, or downward deflection, increases in magnitude after a myocardial infarction. The range of normal for the QRS amplitude is rather large. Remember, amplitude of the R wave is a reflection of the size (mass) of the myocardium sensed by that particular lead. Therefore, if the ventricles are large, the R will be of high amplitude. For most of you, this will be a good thing, as it shows that you are in good cardiovascular condition. (Exercise, such as running or swimming enlarges the heart.) If a person has not been exercising, enlargement of the myocardium may be the sign of a disorder such as hypertension, where the heart has to work harder against the higher resistance pressure in the arteries. Low potassium flattens the T wave while elevated serum potassium levels increases the size of the T wave. Think of the T wave as a "tent" over potassium ions. Is it empty or full? Potassium can be lost due to excessive sweating or by ingestion of certain diuretics.

The amplitude as well as the shape of the waves varies depending on electrode placement and how much electricity due to muscle mass is "seen" by the electrode(s) recording. The duration of the events is not influenced by electrode position.

The standard bipolar limb leads were devised by Einthoven in 1908 and designated Leads I, II, and III as illustrated. **Leads** are always specific combinations of recording electrodes. The EKG set up requires a guard (ground) electrode, attached to the right leg, and two recording electrodes.

Lead I records the potential of the left arm minus the potential of the right arm. (Flow of electricity from right to left arm. **Lead II** records the potential of the left leg minus the potential of the right arm (flow of electricity from right arm to left leg). As the heart is normally angled slightly to the left, this lead normally picks up the most electricity as it passes over the most mass. This is why Lead II is the standard limb lead and is the one we will make most of our measurements from today. **Lead III** represents the potential of the left leg minus that of the left arm (flow of electricity from left arm to left leg). The potential differences measured simultaneously from these three bipolar leads has the relation II = I + III. All of the recordings from these leads should deflect the pen upward.

It has often been observed that in some cases, the amplitude of Lead I is higher than that of Lead II. This usually means that the heart is wider than it is long and so more mass is measured by Lead I. Often, also, Lead III may be higher than Lead II. This usually means that the heart is positioned more up and down than angled to the left. Sometimes, looking at the person makes these differences not so surprising. (ex: Tall, thin students often have a high Lead III).

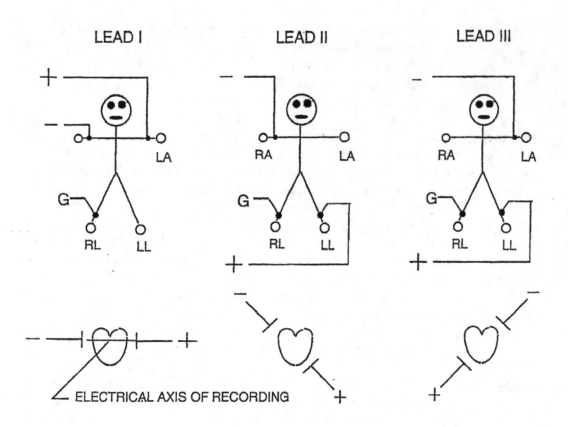

Figure 4. Electrode arrangement for standard EKG limb leads.

Another system of leads commonly used is the **augmented unipolar limb lead** developed by Frank Wilson. In this type of recording, two of the limb leads are connected through appropriate electrical resistors to the negative terminal of the electrocardiograph while the third limb is connected to the positive terminal. Wilson found that with these lead setups the voltage in the electrocardiograph machine had to be amplified, "augmented", in order to get tracing of similar magnitude as those from leads I, II, or III.

Three augmented leads are commonly used:

> **AVR (Augmented Vector Right) - right arm positive**
> **AVL (Augmented Vector Left) - left arm positive**
> **AVF (Augmented Vector Foot) - left leg (foot) positive**

In lead AVR, the electricity of the heart moves from the right, where it originates in the SA node, to the left side of the atria. The positive recording electrode is on the right arm and thus "sees" the electricity moving away. The pen will deflect downward with this lead. This is why AVR is always inverted!

The combination of three bipolar and three unipolar leads provides a view of the heart's electrical activity from six different angles on the frontal plane. This hexagonal reference system allows

EKG 4- 6

precise evaluation of the direction of the vector attributed to the spread of the depolarization through the ventricles within the two dimensions of the frontal plane.

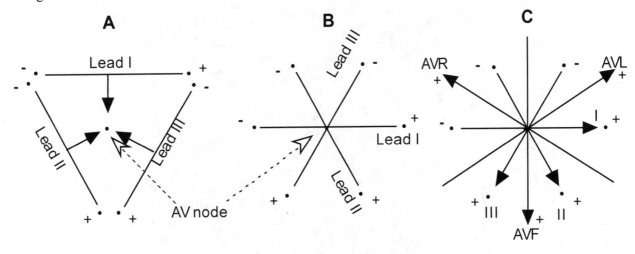

Figure 5. Einthoven's triangle and lead vectors. Leads I, II, and III can be visualized as forming a triangle around the heart on the body's frontal plane with the AV node in the center.

The heart is a three dimensional organ. To increase the diagnostic value of EKGs in a clinical setting, additional recordings are made from at least six lead positions on the chest. The **chest leads (precordial leads)** provide observation points on the horizontal plane. Leads in certain positions are better able to pick up slight variations in the heart's conduction system. If we visualize the electrodes as though they were attached to the surface of a sphere surrounding the heart, the 12 lead EKG "takes pictures" of the heart from 12 different angles of view. Although our equipment is capable of recording the 6 chest leads, we will not be recording these due to time constraints and modesty issues.

The direction of the R wave, whether up or down particularly in Leads I and AVF, are useful in determining the electrical axis of the heart. The **axis of the heart** refers to the direction of depolarization which spreads throughout the heart stimulating the myocardium to contract. This reflects the orientation of the heart within the chest.

Vectors are used to illustrate the direction of this electrical activity. The **mean QRS vector** considers both the magnitude and direction of ventricular depolarization. The mean QRS vector begins in the AV node and normally points downward and to the left because the heart is usually oriented down and to the left. The mean QRS vector will shift if the heart is displaced in the chest, as may occur with obesity. Hypertrophy of one ventricle will shift the vector toward that side, while a myocardial infarction will shift the vector way from the area that has lost its blood supply.

Leads I and AVF are particularly sensitive to the heart's axis. Imagine a sphere around the heart with its center the AV node. As the positive wave of depolarization spreads within the heart from right to left toward the positive electrode on the left arm, you will see the typical positive, upward, deflection of the R wave on the EKG. If the R wave is pointing downward, this means that the positive recording electrode on the left arm is not "seeing" the signal coming toward it

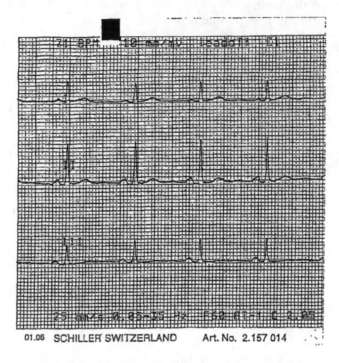

Figure 6. Normal electrocardiograms recorded from leads I, II, and II and the standard bipolar leads.

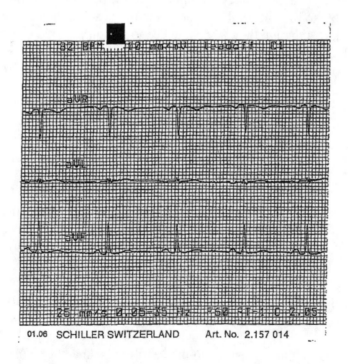

Figure 7. Normal electrocardiograms recorded from the three augmented unipolar limb leads, AVR, AVL and AVF.

properly. This is due to a **right axis deviation**. If both Lead I and AVF point down, this indicates an **extreme right axis deviation** wherein neither lead is "seeing" a typical signal.

In Lead AVF, the R wave is normally positive (pointing upward). When the R wave on Lead AVF is negative (pointing down) the electrode on the left leg is not "seeing" the proper orientation. This indicates a **left axis deviation.** (see Figure 9)

Applying the same principles to an analysis of the chest leads would permit determination of whether the heart's axis points anteriorly as is normal or deviates to the posterior.

It is imperative that you be familiar with the normal function of the heart in order to develop even a limited understanding of the electrocardiogram. Refer to your textbook's presentation of the cardiac cycle and electrical activity of the heart.

Procedures

Electrocardiography

Your instructor will demonstrate the following procedures for the class and will be available to help you with the set ups when you are working in your group. The instructor may also choose to demonstrate the effects of exercise or other stimuli on an EKG with a volunteer.

A. Directions for Schiller AT-1 Electrocardiograph

1. Check that the machine is plugged into the outlet. The green paper light will be on.

2. The subject should be seated comfortably on a laboratory chair with their feet resting on the floor or on the rung of the chair.

3. Attach the Schiller "Biotab" electrodes to the inside of both wrists and ankles, being careful to place the electrode on a fleshy spot and not a bone. You may have to remove the subject's watch. If the subject used lotion recently, it should be wiped away using an alcohol wipe before applying the electrode. The smaller end that does not have adhesive should be pointing distally (away).

4. Attach electrode clips to the right arm (**RA** = white), left arm (**LA** = black), right leg (**RL** = green) and left leg (**LL** = red). The right leg is the ground!

   a. Make sure that the clips do not pull the tabs away from the skin.

   b. If the tabs do not stick well, use a piece of yellow tape to secure them to the skin.

5. Make sure the subject is relaxed, breathing normally with arms resting on their legs and legs resting on the floor or on the rung of the chair. Any skeletal muscle activity will interfere with the recording.

6. Press the **ON** button. Press **10mm/mv** (button 5). Press **25 mm/s** (button 2)

7. Press the **triangular lead selector** pointer up to select leads I, II and III.

8. Press **MANUAL PRINT**. Record for 2 strip lengths (about 7 seconds). Press **STOP**.

9. Press the **triangular lead selector** pointer down to select leads aVR, aVL and aVF.

10. Press **MANUAL PRINT**. Again, record for 2 strip lengths. Press **STOP**.

11. If your reading does **NOT** appear to be normal, the operator should contact the instructor before unhooking the subject's electrodes! The most common causes of apparent abnormalities are improper placement of electrodes, electrodes not seated tightly, movement of the subject, and the subject's use of lotion which impedes the signal to the electrode. Electrical activity of skeletal muscle will be picked up as background waves on the EKG. Deep breathing by the subject will cause the recording to drift in large waves.

12. If time permits, remove the clips from the tabs and have the subject exercise for two minutes on the stationary bicycle, then re-record the EKG on all 6 leads.

13. If everything appears normal, remove clips and discard tabs. Put your name on your recording.

Interpretation of the EKG

A. Determining the Heart Rate from an EKG

A quick way to estimate the heart rate is to look at the distance separating two adjacent QRS waves.

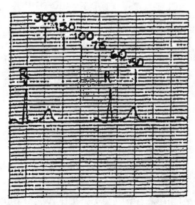

Figure 8. Rapid estimation of heart rate from an EKG. In this example the second R wave falls between 60 and 75, so the rate is estimated at about 66 beats/min.

1. Find a QRS with the R setting on a heavy red line or as close as possible on Lead I.

2. Move one dark line over and label the heavy red lines to the right "300, 150, 100, 75, 60, and 50" as seen in Figure 8. (Clinicians memorize them as triplets: 300, 150, 100 then 75, 60, and 50.)

3. Starting with the QRS on the line look to where the next R wave falls and estimate the rate. Most of the time the next R will fall between two dark lines. Remember there are 5 boxes between each dark line. To determine how many beats each box represents use the following formula:

   (Dark line heart rate 1 − Dark line heart rate 2) / 5 = Heart beats per box
   (ex. (75 − 60) / 5 = 3 heart beats per box between 75 and 60)

   Add the number of estimated beats between the dark lines to Dark line heart rate 2.

4. Compare the rate determined by this method with the heart rate printed on the EKG paper.

5. Repeat for Lead II and Lead III.

6. Determine the heart rates of 3 other students in the class using the rapid method.

7. Record your results in the POST-LAB RESULTS AND OBSERVATIONS section.

B. Duration of P, QRS and T waves and associated intervals

1. On **Lead II** of your EKG, measure the duration of the following events by counting the number of horizontal boxes for each event. Use Figure 3 as a guide.

   P wave
   QRS interval
   T wave
   P-R interval (NOTE: the downward Q deflection is often missing, thus PQ interval = PR interval)
   S-T segment
   S-T interval
   Q-T interval

2. Record your results in the appropriate table in the POST-LAB RESULTS AND OBSERVATIONS section.

3. Calculate the duration of each event in seconds by multiplying the number of boxes by 0.04 seconds. We set the Schiller EKG machine to 25mm/sec, so each small 1 mm box is equivalent to 0.04 seconds on the horizontal.

4. Record your duration in seconds in the table.

5. Compare your measurements to the normal values in Table 1.

6. If your value falls within the normal range, you are normal and you will do no additional work.

7. If a value is outside the normal range you should determine the percentage deviation of your measurement from the mean. This is obtained by dividing your value by the mean value and then multiplying the quotient by 100.

8. If any of your duration values appear to be outside the normal range, see the instructor. If they are truly abnormal, see your physician.

Table 1. Normal EKG Time Measurements for Adults at Normal Heart Rate. Lead II.

	Normal Range (seconds)	Mean (seconds)
P wave	0.07 - 0.12 (0.06 - 0.11)	(0.08)
QRS interval	0.05 - 0.10 (0.06 - 0.11)	0.08
T wave	(0.12 - 0.20)	(0.16)
P-Q or P-R interval	0.12 - 0.20	0.18
S-T interval (QT minus QRS)		0.32
Q-T interval	0.26 - 0.45	0.40 (0.34)

From: Best & Taylor's Physiological Basis of Medical Practice. Numbers in () from Experimental Physiology and Pharmacology, a lab manual from Loyola Univ. School of Dentistry, 1987.

C. Wave Amplitude

1. On Lead II of your EKG, measure the amplitude of the P, QRS and T wave by counting the number of vertical boxes for each event. The amplitude of the QRS complex is from the top of the R to bottom of the S wave.

2. Record your results in the appropriate table in the POST-LAB RESULTS AND OBSERVATIONS section.

3. Calculate the amplitude of each event in millivolts by multiplying the number of boxes by 0.1 millivolts. We set the Schiller EKG machine to 10mm/mv, so each small 1 mm box is equivalent to 0.1 millivolts on the vertical.

4. Record your amplitude in millivolts in the table.

5. Compare your measurements to the normal values in Table 2.

6. If your value falls within the normal range, you are normal and you will do no additional work.

7. If a value is outside the normal range you should determine the percentage deviation of your measurement from the mean. This is obtained by dividing your value by the mean value and then multiplying the quotient by 100.

8. If any of your duration values appear to be outside the normal range, see the instructor. If they are truly abnormal, see your physician.

9. Repeat for the QRS of Lead I and Lead III.

Table 2. Values for signal amplitudes in millivolts (mv). Lead II only.

	Range[L]	Mean Value[L]	Lead II Usual Values[G]
P wave:	0.02 - 0.22 mv	0.10 mv	0.1 - 0.3 mv
QRS wave:	0.07 - 2.12 mv	1.00 mv	1.0 mv
T wave:	0.04 - 0.56 mv	0.30 mv	0.2 - 0.3 mv

From: [G]Guyton, Textbook of Medical Physiology; [L]Experimental Physiology and Pharmacology, Loyola Univ.

D. Electrical axis of the heart

1. Look at the R waves of your Lead I and Lead AVF to determine the electrical axis of your heart. Compare them to Figure 9.

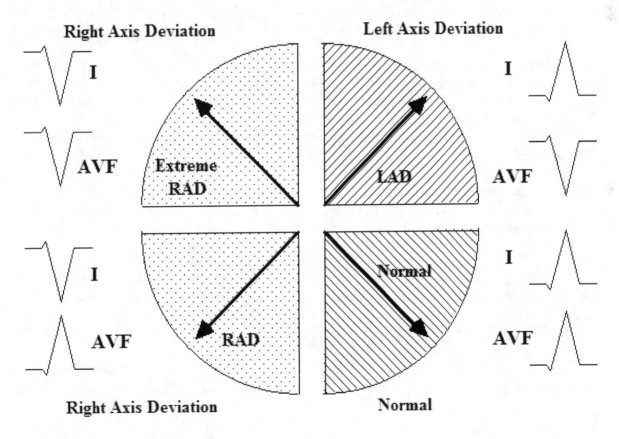

Figure 9. Axis of the Heart Determination.

2. If the R wave is deflected upwards (positive), record as a +. If it is deflected downward, record as a -. Confirm the direction the R wave is deflected by looking at the P and T waves.

3. Record your results in the appropriate section in the POST-LAB RESULTS AND OBSERVATIONS section.

4. If they both do not point upwards, see the instructor. If there is truly a deviation, see your physician.

II. HEART SOUNDS

Introduction

The heart is a quiet pump but it is not silent. Blood moving through the chambers and rushing through the valves makes noise. The closing of heart valves to prevent backflow generates most of the lub-dupp sound we associate with the heart beat.

When heart valves close, the flaps of the valves and surrounding fluids vibrate due to pressure differentials. These sounds travel from the heart through surrounding tissues and resonant on the chest wall as a sound board. We will use the **stethoscope** to listen in on the heart at the surface of the chest. Listening to body sounds, usually with the aid of a stethoscope, is called **auscultation**.

As the ventricles enter systole, the blood inside is put under increasing pressure. It catches behind the cusps of the atrioventricular valves (tricuspid and bicuspid) forcing them shut. The closure of the A-V valves produces the **first heart sound, (S1)** which makes the sound **"lub"**. Most of the sound's intensity is thought to be due to the vibration of the taut chordae tendineae and valve cusps immediately after closure rather than the edges of the valves slapping together initially upon closing.

The **second heart sound, (S2)** which sounds like **"dupp"**, is of somewhat higher pitch and shorter duration than the first. The dupp sound is caused by the closing of the aortic and pulmonary semilunar valves. Here again most of the sound comes from the vibrations of the taut valves after closing.

The lub sound occurs when the ventricle is starting its contraction (systole) and the dupp sound follows when the ventricle is starting to relax (diastole). Valves open slowly and make no noise. After the second heart sound there is a longer pause before the cycle repeats itself. We might say it as lub – dupp – pause, lub – dupp – pause, etc.

A **heart murmur** is an abnormal sound associated with some pathology. A tape of murmurs will be available for you to listen to.

Procedure

1. Use the stethoscope to listen to the sounds of your own heart. Listen at all four points shown in Figure 10.

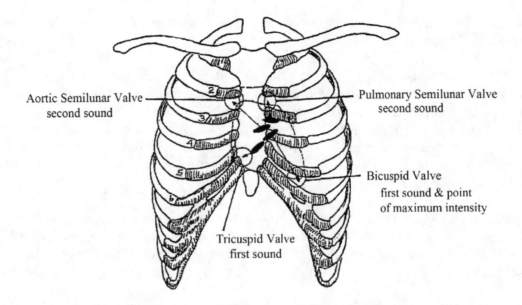

Figure 10. Anterior view of the thorax. Circles represent surface areas where heart valve sounds are heard best. Outline and black ovals are projections of heart and valves to surface.

2. Listen to the recording of abnormal heart sounds if time permits.

III. BLOOD PRESSURE

Introduction

In order to flow, the blood must be under pressure. There is measurable pressure throughout the entire closed circulatory system. For clinical purposes, blood pressure is usually measured in the brachial artery.

The volume of blood in the arteries determines the pressure exerted by the blood against the arterial walls. Arterial blood volume is determined by **cardiac output**, which is the amount of blood the heart pumps into the system each minute, and by the **peripheral resistance**. Peripheral resistance depends on the viscosity of the blood and the length of the arterioles. Resistance is also influenced by the diameter and elasticity of the arteries.

Each time the ventricles contract (**systole**) blood surges under pressure into the arteries causing them to stretch. **Systolic pressure** is a measure of the force exerted by the blood against the walls of the arteries when the heart is contracted. The systolic pressure should normally range between 90 and 140 mm Hg. **Diastole** is the period in the cardiac cycle when the heart is relaxed and filling with blood. The **diastolic pressure** is maintained by the elastic recoil of the arteries, and it should range between 60 and 90 mm Hg. Diastolic pressure is then a measure of peripheral resistance and gives information about the condition of peripheral vessels. This is why an increased diastolic pressure at rest above 95 mmHg is often an indicator of **arteriosclerosis** (hardening of the arteries).

Lowered peripheral resistance allows the blood to "escape" from the heart and large arteries more quickly, reducing arterial blood volume and thus reducing the blood pressure. This is why a normal healthy individual with elastic arteries will have a low resting blood pressure. They tend to also have a lower heart rate as their heart enlarges with exercise. During exercise the cardiac output increases and the peripheral resistance does not change markedly. We would thus normally expect a marked increase in systolic blood pressure and a slight increase in diastolic blood pressure during exercise.

Generalized vasodilation or hemorrhaging from large vessels produces a marked drop in peripheral resistance, and blood pressure plummets. This drop in blood pressure is called **"shock"**. When diastolic pressure is insufficient to maintain capillary flow through the brain, the person faints. Shock often leads to death as the brain and all organs are ultimately affected.

Blood pressures are measured in terms of the height of a column of mercury in a glass tube, or manometer. In the early days, one side of the tube would be connected to a hollow needle through stout flexible tubing. The needle would be inserted into an artery, blood filling the tube and pushing against the mercury. The mercury column would rise and fall with each heart beat. This is called the direct method of BP determination. When continuous, pressure readings are required, as during surgery, the direct method is still employed today using catheters.

The blood pressure cuff or **sphygmomanometer**, was later developed for external use. This indirect method depends on the amount of pressure required to close off the flow of blood. This is typically done using the **brachial artery** which runs near the medial side of the humerus in the upper arm.

Pressure gauges should be calibrated against the mercury standard and pressures reported in terms of millimeters of mercury (**mm Hg**) whether the device contains mercury or not. In blood pressure readings we are concerned with two pressures, systolic and diastolic. A systolic pressure of 120mm Hg and a diastolic of 80 mm Hg is written 120/80 and spoken as 120 over 80. Do not forget the units of measurement as mm Hg, even though we all know it and may not say it. We will measure both systolic and diastolic blood pressure.

Pulse pressure is the difference between systolic and diastolic pressure and is normally about 40mm Hg (120 - 80 = 40). The pulse pressure increases with exercise due to increased stroke volume (amount pumped per beat). The increase in stroke volume will largely increase the systolic pressure thus increasing the pulse pressure. In healthy individuals, the increase in pulse pressure during exercise may be even greater as the elastic arteries give less resistance and lower the diastolic reading. In healthy individuals, the pulse pressure will typically return to normal within 10 minutes. If the resting pulse pressure, however, is consistently greater than 40 mmHg, this most likely reflects a decrease in elasticity of the arteries which would raise the systolic number and lower the diastolic number. A large study in 2000 determined that a high pulse pressure is an important risk factor for heart disease.

Mean arterial pressure (MAP) is a weighted average of the systolic and diastolic readings. The mean arterial pressure is equal to the pulse pressure divided by 3 plus the diastolic pressure. Diastolic pressure has a greater effect at rest since the heart is in diastole considerably longer than systole. Usually MAP is in a range of 70-110. If it is less than 60 mmHg delivery of blood to vital organs such as the brain and kidneys may be impaired.

Procedure

1. Two students will need to cooperate on this exercise. One plays the role of the "patient" while the other plays "doctor", then the roles are reversed.

2. The subject should sit comfortably for several minutes with the right arm resting on the lab table.

3. Locate the brachial artery near the inside bend of the elbow. The brachial artery runs between the biceps and triceps.

4. Wrap the completely deflated cuff snugly about the upper arm with the lower edge about an inch above the bend in the elbow.

5. Locate the radial pulse.

6. Close the release valve on the sphygmomanometer by turning it clockwise. While palpating the radial pulse with your fingers, pump the cuff up until the pulse stops.

7. Note the pressure and immediately release the cuff pressure. This is an estimate of systolic pressure. Record it here _____

8. Clean the earpieces of the stethoscope with an alcohol wipe before using it. Place the bell of the stethoscope firmly over the brachial artery below and slightly under the cuff. No sounds should be heard at this time.

9. Close the release valve on the sphygmomanometer by turning it clockwise using your thumb and index finger. Pump pressure into the cuff until the pressure gauge reads about 20 - 30 mm Hg pressure above the estimated systolic pressure (from step 7).

10. Open the release valve slightly and let the pressure drop smoothly and slowly at the rate of about 2 to3 mm Hg per heart beat.

11. Listen through the stethoscope for the first sound. These tapping sounds called the **Korotkoff Sounds** are due to the turbulent flow of blood as it hits the sides of the artery. They indicate that blood is again squeezing past the cuff and will be accompanied by slight oscillation of the pressure indicator. The pressure reading when this soft tapping is first heard is taken as the **systolic pressure.**

12. Continue slowly releasing the pressure and listening. As the pressure is further reduced the tapping sounds increase in intensity, then the sounds become muffled and faint and, when the

vessel is not constricted, eventually cease. The pressure reading when the sound stops is the **diastolic pressure**. Immediately release any remaining pressure!

   a. Usually there is not more than 5 - 10 mm Hg pressure difference between when the sounds become muffled and dull and they disappear. In some individuals the diastolic sound never stops entirely. If this is the case, then the point when the sound first becomes muffled is noted. The blood pressure would then be recorded as 120/80-0.

13. Check the blood pressure two or more times waiting two minutes between readings to allow the arteries to recover their tone. It is common to have an error of $\pm$ 8 mm Hg in individual readings of the systolic and diastolic pressures. Repeat the procedures until you get three rather consistent readings.

14. Record the average of your three most consistent readings in the appropriate table in the POST-LAB RESULTS AND OBSERVATIONS section. Record the subject's values in their own notebook!

15. Record heart rate in the seated individual. You may do this by counting their radial pulse or have them do this by counting their carotid pulse.

16. Once you have your seated readings, measure the pulse rate and blood pressure of your subject immediately upon standing and record the readings in the table in the POST-LAB RESULTS AND OBSERVATIONS section. Have the subject immediately record their heart rate using the carotid artery pulse.

17. Exercise for approximately two minutes or until you detect an effect. (Leave your cuff on while you do so). If you are not feeling well, have asthma or are pregnant, you do not have to do this! If you feel unwell during the exercise interval, stop exercising!

18. Measure blood pressure and pulse rate immediately after exercise and at 2 minutes and 4 minutes after exercising and record these in the POST-LAB RESULTS AND OBSERVATIONS section.

19. Calculate Pulse Pressure and Mean Arterial Pressure and record in POST-LAB RESULTS AND OBSERVATIONS section.

PRE-LAB QUESTIONS

Name _____

1. _____ At rest, the myocardial cell membranes exhibit a charge distribution called the __ .

2. _____ The wave of excitation which sweeps the heart initiating contraction is started by the __ .

3. _____ The term for the reversal in membrane polarity from negative inside to positive inside is called_____

4. _____ A recording of the heart's electrical activity.

5. _____ Depolarization of the atria results in the _ wave on an EKG.

6. _____ In Lead II, the positive electrode is attached to the __ .

7. _____ Which wave of the EKG precedes ventricular systole?

8. _____ The amplitude of an EKG wave reflects the intensity of the charge (mass of myocardium) and is measured in __ .

9. _____ The duration of a wave is a measure of __ and is expressed in __ .

10. _____ The T wave occurs just before what happens in the heart?

11. _____ EKGs are normally recorded at a paper speed of __ , at this rate each millimeter is equivalent to __ seconds.

12. _____ Which Lead is normally always inverted?

13. _____ Which Leads are used to determine if there is an axis deviation?

"Clinical Thinking": How would late pregnancy affect the amplitude of Lead I and why?

POST-LAB RESULTS AND OBSERVATIONS

I. ELECTROCARDIOGRAM

1. Tape the Lead I, Lead II, and Lead III EKGs in the space below.
2. On each EKG lead, label the P, QRS, and T waves for one heart cycle.

3. Tape the Lead AVR, Lead AVL, and Lead AVF EKGs in the space below.
4. On each EKG lead, label the P, QRS, and T waves for one heart cycle.

A. Determining the Heart Rate from an EKG (See pg 4-10 – 4-11)

1. Use the rapid method to determine the heart rate for:

Lead II _____ beats/min.   Printed rate _____ beats/min.

Lead AVL _____ beats/min.   Printed rate _____ beats/min.

2. Look at EKGs of three other students' Lead II and use the rapid method to estimate their heart rate. Compare with the rate printed on the EKG

	My estimate	Printed rate
Student 1	_____	_____
Student 2	_____	_____
Student 3	_____	_____

B. Duration of P, QRS and T waves and associated intervals (See pg 4-11 – 4-12)

	Length (mm) #boxes	Time (seconds) X 0.04 sec	% Deviation
P wave			
QRS interval			
T wave			
P-R interval (PQ interval)			
S-T segment			
S-T interval (QT minus QRS)			
Q-T interval			

Remember, you only need to calculate % deviation by dividing your value by the mean if you are out of the normal range!

If you are out of the normal range see the instructor. If you are really out of the normal range, see your physician!

C. Wave Amplitude (See pg 4-12 – 4-13)

	Height (mm) #boxes	Millivolts X 0.1 mV	% Deviation from Normal for Lead II only
Lead II P wave			
Lead II QRS complex			
Lead II T wave			
Lead I QRS complex			
Lead III QRS complex			

Only calculate % deviation if your values are out of the normal range. If so, see the instructor.

1. Add your Lead I QRS and Lead III QRS millivolts. _____

   The potential differences (millivolts) measured simultaneously from the three bipolar leads should have the relationship II = I + III.

2. Did Lead I QRS plus Lead III QRS equal Lead II QRS? _____

D. Electrical axis of the heart (See pg 4-13)

1. Lead I QRS _____ (+ or -)   AVF lead QRS _____ (+ or -).

2. Circle the quadrant of Figure 9 that your Lead I and Lead AVF most looks like

Upper left	Upper right
Lower left	Lower right

3. Does this represent a deviation or is it normal? _____

E. EKG after exercise

1. If you recorded your EKG after exercise, which amplitudes and intervals changed?

2. What was the heart rate? _____ Pulse pressure_____

II. HEART SOUNDS

1. Listen to your own and also to the recording of abnormal sounds.

III. BLOOD PRESSSURE

A. Resting

POSITION	PULSE RATE	SYSTOLIC PRESSURE	DIASTOLIC PRESSURE	PULSE PRESSURE	MEAN ARTERIAL PRESSURE
Sitting					
Standing					

B. After Exercise

TIME	PULSE RATE	SYSTOLIC PRESSURE	DIASTOLIC PRESSURE	PULSE PRESSURE	MEAN ARTERIAL PRESSURE
End of exercise					
After 2 minutes					
After 4 minutes					

Page Deliberately Left Blank

RESPIRATORY SYSTEM AND METABOLISM

HISTORY

According to Plato and Aristotle, the function of breathing was merely to cool the fire (*flamma vitalis*) that burned within the heart. No real progress was made on the role of respiration until the true circulation of the blood was worked out by William Harvey and others in the 17th century. Robert Boyle (of Boyle's gas Law) and Robert Hooke, through animal experimentation, proved that an animal could not live without air and an animal with an open chest could be kept alive if air was forced into its trachea with a bellows.

Antoine Lavoisier, in 1777, confirmed the nature of oxygen and in fact gave it its name. He showed that it was in inspired air while carbon dioxide was in expired air. Sadly, despite this and many other scientific contributions, he was sent to the guillotine during the French Revolution.

The Eustachian tube was described in Bartolomeo Eustachio's book *The Examination of the Organ of Hearing* published in 1562. Interestingly, the respiratory system itself is almost completely devoid of eponyms with the best known eponym being the "Adam's apple" or thyroid cartilage of the larynx.

OBJECTIVES

1. To identify and learn the function of the major organs of the respiratory system.
2. To identify the microscopic structure of the trachea and the lungs.
3. To determine human lung capacities.
4. To examine the effects various activities upon the ability to hold one's breath.
5. To estimate the resting metabolic rate.

I. GROSS ANATOMY

Introduction

The respiratory system of mammals consists of the nasal passages, pharynx, larynx, trachea, and lungs. The structures of the respiratory system can be structurally grouped as the **upper respiratory tract** which is all structures superior to the vocal cords and all structures inferior to the vocals cords, the **lower respiratory tract**. These structures deliver oxygen to the blood for distribution to all cells and also function in the elimination of carbon dioxide. The **conduction system** is a series of tubes that deliver the air to the lungs and the **respiratory membrane** is where oxygen and carbon dioxide are exchanged between the air and bloodstream.

Air is taken into the body or **ventilated** through the **nose**. The nose has external openings called the **external nares (nostrils)**. The air will enter the external nares into the **vestibule** of the nose and continue into the right and left **nasal cavities**. As the air travels though the nasal cavities, it is warmed, humidified, and filtered as it passes over the mucous membranes of the **superior, middle and inferior nasal conchae** on the lateral walls of the nasal cavities. The air passes between the conchae through the superior, middle and inferior meatuses, tube like grooves between the conchae. Air exits the nasal cavities through the **internal nares (choanae)** and passes into the pharynx.

The **pharynx** is a muscular tube that is divided into three regions; the **nasopharynx**, the **oropharynx**, and the **laryngopharynx**. The nasopharynx extends from the internal nares to the tip of the soft palate and should be a passageway for air only. Air can travel from the nasopharynx to the middle ear through the **Eustachian (auditory) tube**s. Immune system tissues, the **pharyngeal tonsils (adenoids)**, are found in the superior wall of the nasopharynx. Other immune system tissues, the palatine tonsils and lingual tonsils, are found in the oropharynx, which extends from the soft palate to the epiglottis. The oral cavity will open into the oropharynx through the **fauces**. The last section of the pharynx is the laryngopharynx, which extends from the epiglottis to the cricoid cartilage. The laryngopharynx terminates at the larynx anteriorly and the esophagus posteriorly.

The **larynx** (voice box) is a structure that connects the pharynx with the trachea. It is also the site of vocal sound production. The larynx is supported by a collection of cartilage structures. The largest cartilage structure is the **thyroid cartilage** (Adam's apple). Other cartilage structures include the **cricoid cartilage**, and the paired **arytenoid**, **corniculate**, and **cuneiform cartilages**. The entrance into the larynx is called the **glottis** and it is protected by another cartilage structure the **epiglottis**. Sound is produced by the larynx as air vibrates the **vocal folds (true vocal cords)**.

Air will continue its journey from the larynx to the **trachea**. The trachea will run anterior to the esophagus and extend from the larynx to approximately the level of the T5 vertebra where it splits into two **primary bronchi**. The right primary bronchus is more vertical, shorter and wider than the left primary bronchus. If we overpower the cough reflex and aspirate particles into the trachea, they tend to lodge in the primary bronchus on the right side. The primary bonchi enter each lung at the **hilus**. The pulmonary arteries and veins also enter and exit the lungs at the hilus.

Each lung is divided by fissures into sections called **lobes**. The right lung has 3 lobes; superior, middle, and inferior, and the left lung has 2 lobes; the superior and inferior lobes. The left lung also has a depression on its medial side, the **cardiac notch**. Each lobe within the lungs is supplied with air by **secondary bronchi**. **Tertiary bronchi**, **bronchioles** and **terminal bronchioles** supply smaller and smaller segments within the lungs. The conduction system ends at the air sacs of the numerous **alveoli**.

Gases diffuse through the thin-walled alveoli into the blood. Blood transports oxygen and nutrients to all the tissues. Oxygen and glucose are used by cells in energy yielding chemical reactions that produce ATP, water, and carbon dioxide. The sum total of all the body's activities may be broadly defined as metabolism. Metabolism includes such things as the building and repairing of tissues, and the storing and using of energy.

Procedure

Refer to the illustrations in your textbook while locating the following structures on any model that shows the structure well. Just because the key doesn't have a number for the structure doesn't mean that you can't see it on the model. Structures grayed out in the table are not shown on that model.

Respiratory Model Keys

Structure Name	Sagittal Section of Head	Respiratory System Plaque	Larynx Model	Torso Model
external nares (nostrils)		1		
vestibule		2		
nasal cavity		3		
superior nasal concha	a			242
middle nasal concha	b			243
inferior nasal concha	c			244
superior meatus				
middle meatus				
inferior meatus				
opening to Eustachian (auditory) tube	d			245
frontal sinus	a	43		
sphenoidal sinus	b	44		
palatine tonsils	q			246
lingual tonsils				
pharyngeal tonsils				
internal naris (choanae)				
pharynx	r			
nasopharynx		4		
oropharynx		5		
laryngopharynx		6		
fauces				
hard palate		9		260
soft palate	h			261
uvula	i	9a		
larynx	X	15		256
epiglottis	I	14	23 & 31	252
glottis				
hyoid bone	12 or k		1	239
thyroid cartilage	II	16	2	258
cricoid cartilage	III	17	3	259
arytenoid cartilage			4	
corniculate cartilage			5	

Structure Name	Sagittal Section of Head	Respiratory System Plaque	Larynx Model	Torso Model
cuneiform cartilage			6	
tracheal cartilages			7	131
thyrohyoid ligament	IV	15	8	253
cricothyroid ligament	V		11	
vocal folds (true vocal cords)	VII	18	28	257
vestibular folds (false vocal cords)	VIII	white line above #18	27	255
trachea	23	19	30	131
trachealis muscle			14	
carina				132
thyroid gland			33	121
esophagus	24			136
left primary bronchus		20		134
left secondary bronchi		21 & 22		
right primary bronchus		23		133
right secondary bronchi		24 & 25		
tertiary bronchi				135
terminal bronchioles		34		
alveoli		35 & 36		
right lung		27		124
right superior lobe				125
right middle lobe				126
right inferior lobe				127
left lung		26		128
left superior lobe				129
left inferior lobe				130
cardiac notch				
apex of lung				
hilus of lung				
pulmonary trunk		31		149
pulmonary arteriole		37		
pulmonary venule		38		
pulmonary veins		46		146
diaphragm		29		70 & 162
esophageal hiatus				
aortic opening				
inferior vena cava opening				

In addition to these models, there are also lung and bronchial tree models that are not numbered. Make sure that you can identify the proper structures on those models also.

Respiration 5- 4

II. MICROSCOPIC ANATOMY

Introduction

The microscopic features of the respiratory system vary depending upon the location within the system. Because the respiratory system opens to the outside of the body, the entire system is lined with a **mucous membrane**. The type of epithelium in the membrane varies. Ciliated pseudostratified columnar epithelial tissue lines the tubes from below the true vocal cords in the larynx through the tertiary bronchioles. In the tertiary bronchioles there is a transition to ciliated simple columnar epithelium and then to simple cuboidal epithelium in the terminal bronchioles. Most of the conducting system has hyaline cartilage in its walls. Bronchioles smaller than 1 mm in diameter do not have cartilage in their walls. Typically there is also a layer of fibrous connective tissue around the tubes that bind them together.

The **mucosa** lines the **lumen** of the trachea and is composed of a layer of **ciliated pseudostratified columnar epithelium** and its underlying lamina propria. Mucus producing **goblet cells** are present in this layer. The epithelial cells sit on the **basement membrane**, which is usually extra thick in the trachea. Below the basement membrane is the **lamina propria** consisting of areolar connective tissue. Below the mucosa is the **submucosa** of areolar connective imbedded with fat and the circular **tracheal glands**. Tracheal glands mainly secrete mucus. Tiny ducts drain the secretions of the mucus glands onto the surface of the mucosa. **Hyaline cartilage** forms the tracheal cartilage rings. The outer connective tissue covering of the trachea is called the **adventitia**. If one considers the cartilage to be part of the adventitia, there would be three layers to the tracheal wall, the mucosa, submucosa and adventitia. This structural pattern continues into the bronchi and bronchioles with the amount of cartilage becoming less in the smaller diameter passageways.

Within the lungs there is a wide variety of tissues, but most of the volume will be the alveolar air sacs. Alveoli are composed of a single layer of **simple squamous epithelium. Lung capillaries** can be found at the edges of the alveoli. These are also composed of simple squamous epithelium. Gases must diffuse through the squamous epithelium and basement membranes of both the capillary and the alveolus. The distance across these two cell layers and the space between them is only 0.5 μM. Any condition that increases the distance of diffusion interferes with the process of gas exchange between the lungs and the blood which is called **external respiration**. The bronchi and bronchioles of the conduction system can also be found within the lungs. Many have hyaline cartilage in their walls. If the bronchi are near the trachea, there will be numerous clusters of purple stained circles of cuboidal cells. These clusters are **mucous glands**, and the lumens of these little glands drain mucus onto the surface of the ciliated epithelium.

Procedure

Trachea

1. Obtain a slide of the trachea. It is labeled "**Pseudostratified ciliated columnar epithelium**". This is a longitudinal section.

2. Using scanning power, find the strip of tissue with ovals of **hyaline cartilage.** You can tell it is hyaline cartilage by the glassy appearance of the matrix. The other strip of tissue on the slide is taken from the back of the trachea and does not usually contain any cartilage.

3. Find the epithelial layer of pseudostratified ciliated columnar epithelium. Focus on it on low and then high power. The smaller rounded cells at the bottom that do not extend up to the surface are the cells which will divide to replace the tall cells when they die.

4. Find the lamina propria that underlies the epithelium.

5. Find the submucosa with the tracheal glands under scanning, low and then high power.

6. Focus on an oval piece of hyaline cartilage under scanning, low and then high power. Notice the **chondrocytes** (cartilage cells) that lie in the spaces called **lacunae.** Notice the glassy pink **extracellular matrix** of the hyaline cartilage. On the surface of the cartilage is the **perichondrium**, a fibrous membrane of irregular dense connective tissue. **Chondroblasts** are those chondrocytes adjacent to the perichondrium. They appear smaller and flattened. Chondroblasts can deposit new cartilage to repair or strengthen a tracheal ring.

7. In the POST- LAB OBSERVATIONS section you will need to draw a section of the trachea with cartilage and label all the structures listed.

Trachea Microscopic Structures

Structure Name
lumen
mucosa
ciliated pseudostratified columnar epithelium
goblet cell
lamina propria
submucosa
tracheal glands
hyaline cartilage
chondroblasts
chondrocytes
lacunae
extracellular matrix
perichondrium
adventitia

Lungs

1. Hold the slide **"Lung Human Bronchioles"** up to the light.

2. View the slide under the scanning objective. Locate a piece of **hyaline cartilage** near the **lumen**.

Respiration 5- 6

3. Identify the **simple columnar epithelium** lining the bronchiole. Between the cartilage and epithelium of the lumen are connective tissue and smooth muscle fibers.

4. You will be able to locate some small arterioles and venules on this slide in the area of the air sacs and alveoli.

5. Locate the **alveoli**. The walls of the alveoli are the very thin pink lines with a lot of white space. Focus on an alveolus. Now switch to low power and then high power (40X). Note that the alveolus is composed of a single layer of **simple squamous epithelium.**

6. Locate an alveolus with an intact adjacent capillary. They are usually smaller and more irregular in shape than the alveoli. Many times they contain blood cells.

7. Identify an alveolar macrophage within an alveolus.

8. In the POST-LAB OBSERVATIONS section make a sketch of an alveolus and capillary and label all the structures listed.

Lung Microscopic Structures

Structure Name
lumen
bronchiole
mucosa
simple columnar epithelium
smooth muscle
hyaline cartilage
alveolus (alveoli)
simple squamous epithelium
capillary
alveolar macrophage

III. LUNG CAPACITIES

Introduction

An individual's metabolism and ability to do stressful physical work is related to the capacity of the lungs. The capacity of the lungs can be divided into four volumes as follows.

A. **Tidal Volume** (TV): the amount of air inhaled and then exhaled during a single normal breath. This volume is usually about 500 ml but is markedly increased during exercise. Athletes have larger TVs.

B. **Inspiratory Reserve Volume** (IRV): the extra air that can be inhaled after a normal inspiration. The average IRV is 3100 ml in males and 1900ml in females.

C. **Expiratory Reserve Volume** (ERV): the ERV of about 1200 ml in males and 700 ml in females is the amount of air that can be forcefully exhaled after a normal passive expiration.

D. **Residual Volume** (RV): the quantity of air adhering to the insides of the air sacs and tubes in the lung. This volume of about 1200 ml in males and 1100 ml in females cannot be exhaled. Measurement of RV requires gas dilution methods and is beyond the scope of this course.

These lung volumes are summed to get useful expressions of lung capacities.

E. **Vital Capacity** (VC): the sum of the first three lung volumes (TV+IRV+ERV). This is the maximum amount of air that can be exchanged by the lungs.

F. **Total Lung Capacity** (TLC): the sum of VC+RV or in other terms TV+IRV+ERV+RV.

Other lung capacities, such as Functional Residual Capacity and Forced Expiratory Volume, are of clinical importance but will not be treated in this exercise.

Procedure

1. Use the **wet spirometer** to measure the capacity of the lungs.

2. Two students will need to cooperate on these tests, one being the observer and the other the subject. The subject sits upright in a chair near the spirometer and must relax as far as possible. Use a new sterile disposable mouthpiece for each subject. Occlude the nasal airway with a noseclip or by pinching the nose and keep eyes closed during a test. The observer will instruct the subject and tabulate spirometer readings.

3. Set the dial of the spirometer to 0 before each test. Repeat each test three times and calculate an average. Notice that the numbers indicate liters, each small line is 0.1 liter or 100 ml (1.2 = 1200 ml).

4. **Measure tidal volume.** Following a normal inspiration, breathe a normal expiration into the spirometer.

5. **Measure inspiratory reserve volume.** Because you cannot inhale using a wet spirometer, you must measure inspiratory reserve volume indirectly. Inhale as deeply as possible and then exhale normally into the spirometer. This is the inspiratory capacity (IC). Enter this number in the IC column. Subtract the tidal volume from this quantity. This amount (remainder) is your inspiratory reserve volume. Enter this value in the inspiratory reserve volume column.

6. **Measure expiratory reserve volume.** Exhale a normal expiration into the room and then exhale all of the air that is left in your lungs into the spirometer. Force out as much as you can.

7. **Measure vital capacity.** Inhale as deeply as possible then forcible exhale as much air as you can into the spirometer. This quantity should equal the sum of measurements of Tidal volume, expiratory reserve volume and inspiratory reserve volume.

8. Record your results in the table in the POST-LAB OBSERVATIONS section.

IV. BREATHING

Introduction

The mechanisms controlling breathing are described in the textbook. The respiratory centers in the pons and medulla are influenced by chemoreceptors monitoring the blood levels of CO_2, pH, and oxygen. When a person holds their breath, the concentration of CO_2 increases which causes the respiratory center to initiate inspiration. A similar mechanism is simultaneously influencing heart rate.

The muscles involved in quiet breathing are the external intercostals and the diaphragm. The phrenic nerve innervates the diaphragm and leaves the spinal cord from C3-C5. The intercostal nerves control the intercostal muscles and leave the spinal cord at T1-T12. A spinal cord injury at C7 would allow the diaphragm to work, but not the intercostals. These nerves are Somatic nerves not Autonomic nerves as the muscles involved in breathing are skeletal (voluntary) muscle, not smooth muscle. Smooth muscle is found lining the airways and so sympathetic stimulation would result in relaxation of this muscle and dilation of the airways. When we breathe deeply in, the scalene and sternocleidomastoid muscles are also activated. During a forced exhale the internal intercostals and abdominal muscles are activated.

Procedure

1. Attach a pulse oximeter to one of your fingers. Record your pulse rate and your oxygen saturation levels.

2. In a seated and rested position, inhale maximally and hold your breath for as long as possible. Record the elapsed time and your pulse rate and oxygen saturation levels. After a pause for recovery, repeat this procedure two more times, and determine an average.

3. Because of lab safety concerns, you will do this procedure in the hall just outside of lab. Place a straw in a paper cup filled with tap water. Repeat procedure 1. This time, just before you start to gasp for breath after holding as long as possible, start to sip the water through the straw and swallow. Record the total time you were able to hold your breath. Expect to be able to hold your breath longer this time. This protective reflex is termed **deglutition apnea**.

4. After fully recovering from the above procedure, hyperventilate before holding your breath. Take 20 deep breaths exhaling fully after each. As you inhale maximally and hold it for as long as possible, record your oxygen saturation levels. Record your time as in previous test.

Sit on a chair rather than the stools for this test. WATCH YOUR PARTNER, do not let them faint and fall.

5. Obtain a sack; hold it tightly over your mouth and nose and breathe in it for one minute. Record your oxygen saturation levels. Take a deep breath from the sack and hold it as long as possible. Record the elapsed time.

6. Your partner will count your breathing rate at rest for three one-minute intervals. The subject should be reading or at least not concentrating on the act of breathing. Record the results and calculate the average.

V. METABOLISM

Introduction

When fuels are oxidized in cells, oxygen is used and carbon dioxide is produced in proportion to the energy yield. To estimate an animal's metabolic rate either the oxygen consumption or carbon dioxide production is measured. It is also possible to estimate the energy yield by measuring the heat loss.

Procedure

1. The surface of the body is the principal route of heat loss. Determine your body surface area using the nomogram provided in lab. Record your value in the POST-LAB OBSERVATIONS section.

2. Numerous studies have related heat loss measurements to metabolic rates allowing the construction of Table 1 provided in lab. Multiply your calculated body surface area by the value from Table 1 to estimate your basal metabolic rate and record in the POST-LAB OBSERVATIONS.

3. We now wish to determine how much oxygen must be provided to the mitochondria in order for them to carry out the cell respiration reactions yielding this level of basal metabolism. Each liter of oxygen used in the mitochondria's electron transport system, yields 4.83 kcal of energy. Go to the POST-LAB OBSERVATIONS section and complete the required calculations.

    Remember, for our procedures we are using average values. In a clinical situation, equipment is available to measure heat loss and/or oxygen consumption directly for the patient when this information is needed.

PRE-LAB QUESTIONS   **Name** _____

Use your textbook or other resource to answer these questions before you come to lab.

A. Give a function for the following structures:

    1. epiglottis

    2. larynx

    3. diaphragm

B. What effect would result from stimulation of the tracheal and bronchial smooth muscles by sympathetic nerves? _____

C. Which nerve stimulates the diaphragm for inhalation? _____

    1. Where does it branch off the spinal cord? _____

    2. Is this nerve a part of the Autonomic Nervous System? _____

D. Besides the diaphragm, what muscles are principally involved in normal tidal inhalation?

E. List the muscles activated when we take a very deep breath.

F. List the muscles involved in a forced exhalation.

G. Where in the CNS are the control centers for breathing?

H. From the History: Who gave Oxygen its name and what happened to him?

I. GROSS ANATOMY

A. Sagittal section of the head. Label all structures. (The structures of the larynx are difficult to identify here!! They are best seen on the separate larynx model!)

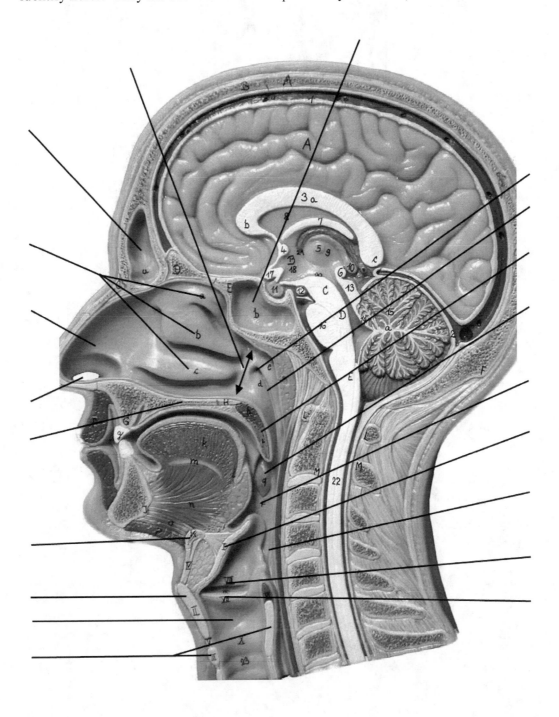

B. Larynx, trachea and bronchi, anterior view. Label all structures.

Right side

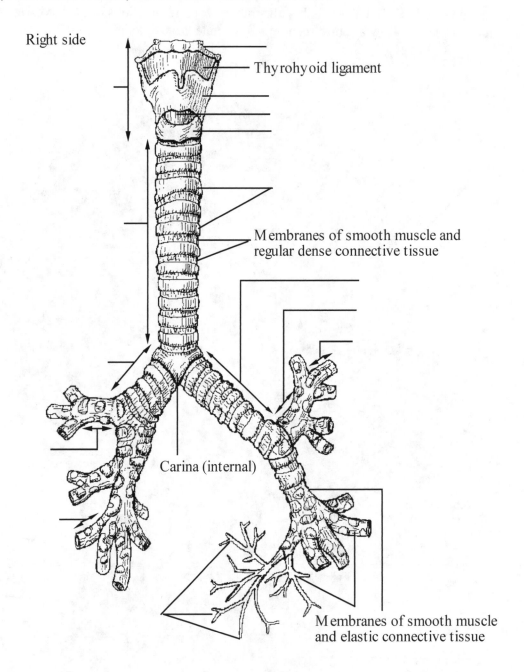

Thyrohyoid ligament

Membranes of smooth muscle and
regular dense connective tissue

Carina (internal)

Membranes of smooth muscle
and elastic connective tissue

III. LUNG CAPACITIES

A. Lung volumes. Note your units of measurement, either L = liters, or ml = milliliters

	Tidal Volume (TV)	Inspiratory Capacity (IC)	Inspiratory Reserve Volume (IRV) (IC-TV)	Expiratory Reserve Volume (ERV)	Total = TV+ERV+IRV	Vital Capacity (VC)
Trial 1					███	
Trial 2					███	
Trail 3					███	
Average		███				

For Total = column add the averages of columns 1, 3 & 4. This sum should be very close to the average of the Vital capacity column if you performed the measurements of TV, ERV and IRV properly. If this sum is 1000 ml different than VC, you should repeat your measurements of TV, ERV and IRV.

B. Compare your average vital capacity measured directly with the average total of TV+ERV+IRV (last row, columns 5 & 6).
  1. Explain why there may be differences between the two values.

  2. Which method do you feel is more accurate? Give some possible answers as to why.

C. Compare the predicted VC of an "average" normal individual to your measured VC. Charts are available showing average vital capacity values for individuals of different height and age. Males and females require different charts. Multiply your height in inches by 2.54 to convert to centimeters.

_____ / _____ X 100 = _____ % of normal
Measured vital capacity   Predicted capacity

    1. Why do you think the measured vital capacity is the same or different from the predicted capacity?

IV. BREATHING

A. Compare the length of time you were able to hold your breath under four trial conditions and account for the differences. As you are completing the breath holding exercise, also record your pulse rate and oxygen saturation.

	Breath Holding Time	Pulse Rate	Oxygen Saturation
At rest	███████████████		
Breath holding			
Trial 1			
Trial 2			
Trial 3			
Average of Trials			
Sipping Water			
Hyperventilating			
Breathing into a sack			

B. List in the space below the reasons the elapsed times for after sipping water, hyperventilating, or breathing into a sack differed from the average of the trials.

C. Breathing Rate at Rest.

Trial 1 _____

Trial 2 _____

Trial 3 _____

Average _____

V. METABOLISM

A. Determine your predicted metabolic rate

    1. Determine your body surface area using the nomogram chart provided in lab.

       Body surface area = _____ m^2.

    2. Multiply the body surface area value by the factor from the provided table in order to estimate your basal metabolic rate.

       _____ m^2 X _____ kcal/hr/ m^2 = _____ kcal/hr
       body surface area   Table 1 factor

       This is your estimated metabolic rate in kcal/hour based on body surface area. Determine your total energy requirements if basal metabolism were maintained for 24 hours.

    3. Multiply your predicted metabolic rate in Kcal/hour based on body surface area by 24 hours/day

       _____ kcal/hr X 24 = _____ kcal/day

       This is the energy equivalent of what we need to eat to stay alive. A sedentary life style may only require an additional 500 calories.

B. Estimation of oxygen requirements

    1. Divide your kcal metabolic rate value by 4.83 (remember the resulting quotient will be in the units of liters of oxygen per hour.)

       _____ kcal/ hr x 1 liter O_2/ 4.83 kcal = _____ liters O_2 /hour
       (Your metabolic rate)   (Your estimated O_2 consumption)

       This is your estimated hourly oxygen requirement at basal level.

    2. At this rate, how many liters of oxygen will you need each day? _____

C. Critical Thinking

    1. What biological reactions release oxygen to the environment? _____

URINARY SYSTEM ANATOMY

HISTORY

The gross anatomy of the urinary system was described with clarity and in great detail by Aristotle in the third century BC in *Historia Animalium*. No new knowledge was added for two millennia and, on the contrary, much was lost. Microscopic anatomy had to wait for the development of the microscope, perfected in the 1600s by Antony van Leeuwenhoek. The ball-shaped capillary bed known as the glomerulus was discovered by Marcello Malpighi in 1659. William Bowman, an English surgeon, described the capsule that bears his name in 1842 and Friedrich Henle, a German microscopic anatomist, described the loop in 1862.

OBJECTIVES

1. To learn the gross anatomy of the urinary system and the primary functions of the major organs.
2. To examine some of the urinary system organs with a microscope.
3. To get an introduction to urinary physiology using a computer lab simulation program.

I. GROSS ANATOMY OF THE URINARY SYSTEM

Introduction

To maintain the constant internal conditions known as homeostasis, an organism not only needs to provide nutrients to all its cells but also must dispose of their wastes. The principal waste products are carbon dioxide from cellular respiration, nitrogenous wastes from protein catabolism, and salts. The respiratory system disposes of most of the carbon dioxide. A proper concentration of water in the body must also be maintained. The urinary system maintains both salt and water balance while ridding the body of nitrogen wastes and excess normal constituents. It also performs many other functions such as regulating red blood cell production using Erythropoetin and blood pressure, using Renin. It also helps activate Vitamin D.

The urinary system is composed of two kidneys, two ureters, one urinary bladder, and one urethra. The waste products and excess water are made into urine by the kidneys. The urine is transported through the ureters to the urinary bladder and stored there until it is expelled from the body through the urethra.

The kidneys are bean shaped organs found just above the waist and protected by the 11th and 12th rib. The right kidney is positioned slightly lower than the left. The kidneys are **retroperitoneal**, which means they are between the peritoneum and posterior wall of abdomen. Blood vessels, lymphatic vessels, nerves and the ureter enter and exit at the **hilus** of the kidney. The outmost layer of the kidney is the **renal capsule**, a transparent membrane that maintains the shape of the kidney. The functional portion **(parenchyma)** of the kidney includes the renal cortex and the renal medulla. The **renal cortex** is located inside of the renal capsule. The renal medulla is inside of the cortex. The **renal medulla** is comprised of the renal pyramids, renal papillae and renal columns. There are 8-18 cone-shaped **renal pyramids** in the renal medulla; each topped with a **renal papilla** which points toward the center of the kidney. Between the renal pyramids are the renal columns, connective tissue passageways for blood vessels. In the center of each kidney is the **renal sinus** which is filled with the drainage system of the kidneys. Draining each renal papilla is a **minor calyx** (pl. calyces). The minor calyces will drain into **major calyces** which will merge into a single **renal pelvis**. The renal pelvis will empty into the ureter.

The blood supply of the kidneys is extensive. At rest, approximately 25% of the cardiac output is going to the kidneys. Blood enters the kidneys through the renal arteries. Once the **renal artery** enters the kidney it branches into the **segmental arteries** in the renal sinus. As the arteries travel through the renal columns, they are called **interlobar arteries**. The interlobar arteries will curve around and follow the border between the renal cortex and renal medulla. They are now the **arcuate arteries**. Small **cortical radiate** (interlobular) **arteries** will branch off the arcuate arteries projecting into the renal cortex. The **afferent arterioles** branch off the cortical radiate arteries and bring blood into the **glomerulus**, which is the only capillary bed with a name! The **efferent arteriole** takes blood out of the glomerulus and then divides into the **peritubular capillaries** and the **vasa recta** which are capillaries around the loop of Henle. The blood then leaves the kidney via the **cortical radiate** (interlobular) **veins, arcuate veins, interlobar veins** and finally **renal vein**. (See Figure 1.)

The kidney is composed of millions of filter units called **nephrons**. Nephrons are the functional units of the kidney. Each nephron consists of a capsule called **Bowman's capsule (glomerular capsule)**, a **proximal convoluted tubule, loop of Henle (nephron loop)**, and **distal convoluted tubule. Collecting ducts** collect from many distal tubules. These widen into **papillary ducts** which form the renal papilla.

The pressure of the blood is relatively high entering the glomerulus (55 – 60 mmHg) compared to other capillaries (~35 mmHg). Small components of the blood are filtered out of the blood and enter the glomerular (Bowman's) capsule. The remainder of the nephron alters this filtrate by adding toxic components by renal secretion and reabsorbing needed components to return them to the blood. When the altered filtrate leaves the nephron tubules it is called **urine**.

The two ureters connect the renal pelvis of the kidneys to the urinary bladder. Each **ureter** is 10 to 12 inches long, is located retroperitoneal, and enters the posterior wall of the urinary bladder. The **urinary bladder** is a hollow, distensible muscular organ with capacity of 700 - 800 mL. The smooth muscle of the bladder wall is called the **detrusor muscle**. On the floor of the bladder is the **trigone**, a smooth, flat, triangular area that is bordered by the two ureteral openings and the urethral opening. Urine will exit the body through the urethra. The **urethra** in females is quite short, but in males is much longer. The male urethra has three regions: the **prostatic urethra** which passes through the prostate gland, the **intermediate urethra** which passes through the deep muscles of the perineum, and the **spongy urethra** which passes through the penis.

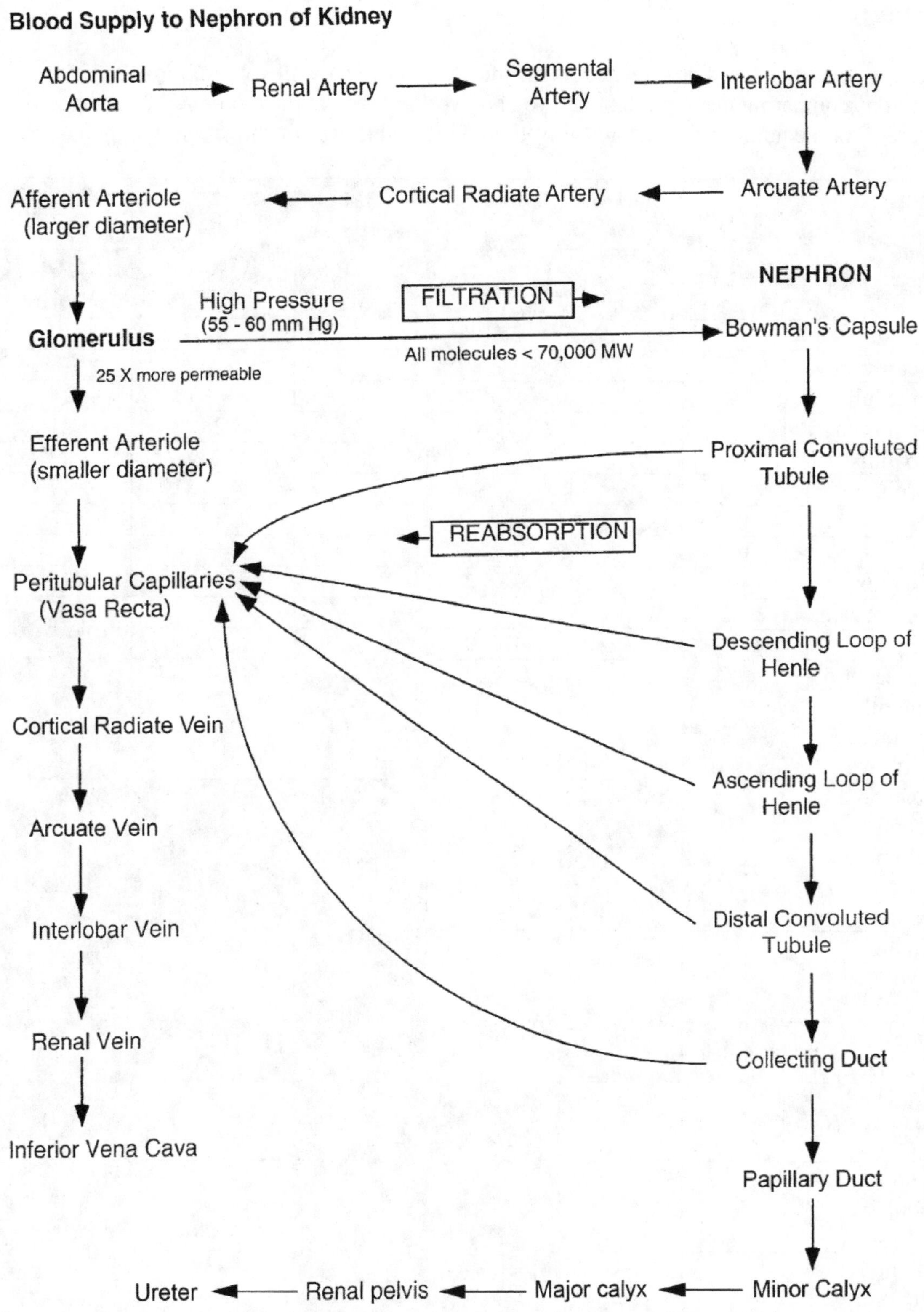

Blood Supply to Nephron of Kidney

Abdominal Aorta → Renal Artery → Segmental Artery → Interlobar Artery
↓
Arcuate Artery → Cortical Radiate Artery → Afferent Arteriole (larger diameter)

NEPHRON

Afferent Arteriole (larger diameter)
↓
Glomerulus

High Pressure (55 - 60 mm Hg) → FILTRATION → Bowman's Capsule
All molecules < 70,000 MW

25 X more permeable
↓
Efferent Arteriole (smaller diameter)
↓
Peritubular Capillaries (Vasa Recta)

REABSORPTION

Bowman's Capsule
↓
Proximal Convoluted Tubule
↓
Descending Loop of Henle
↓
Ascending Loop of Henle
↓
Distal Convoluted Tubule
↓
Collecting Duct
↓
Papillary Duct

Peritubular Capillaries (Vasa Recta)
↓
Cortical Radiate Vein
↓
Arcuate Vein
↓
Interlobar Vein
↓
Renal Vein
↓
Inferior Vena Cava

Ureter ← Renal pelvis ← Major calyx ← Minor Calyx

Figure 1. The blood flow through the kidneys and flow of fluid through the tubular system of the kidney.

Procedure

Locate the structures listed on any model that shows it well. Study all your textbook's illustrations comparing them to the model you are working with at the moment. Learn the structures, not the numbers! Structures grayed out in the table are not shown on that model.

Structure Name	Three Part Kidney Model			Large Kidney Model on stand	Very Large Kidney Model	Male Urinary System Model
	Right Kidney	Nephron	Renal Corpuscle			
right kidney						12
renal capsule						
renal medulla	A			A		14
renal pyramid	7			7	28	21
renal papilla	6			6	16, 20 & 21	22
renal column	20				24 & 31	17
renal sinus						15
renal hilus						23
renal cortex	B			B	22	13
renal corpuscle	12	1				
glomerulus			1 & 8		9	
parietal layer of glomerular (Bowman's) capsule			2 & 10		8	
podocytes - visceral layer of glomerular (Bowman's) capsule			9			
proximal convoluted tubule	11	2a	3			
cuboidal epithelial cell			4			
loop of Henle (nephron loop)	10	3			5	
descending limb of loop of Henle		b			6	
ascending limb of loop of Henle		4c			7	

Structure Name	Three Part Kidney Model			Large Kidney Model on stand	Very Large Kidney Model	Male Urinary System Model
	Right Kidney	Nephron	Renal Corpuscle			
distal convoluted tubule	9	d & 5	11			
macula densa			12			
collecting duct	8	6				
papillary duct	19			19		
minor calyx	5			5	17 & 19	19
major calyx					34	18
renal pelvis	4			4	18	16
ureter	3			3	25	24
urinary bladder						37
rugae						38
trigone						39
prostatic urethra						42
prostate gland						46
detrusor muscle						47
ductus (vas) deferens						49
seminal vesicles						50
adrenal gland					30	11
abdominal aorta						1
right renal artery	2			2	27	4
left renal artery						5
interlobar artery	13				35	
arcuate artery	16	7		16		
cortical radiate artery (red)	14	8		13	10	
afferent arteriole		9	6			
efferent arteriole	15	10	7			
peritubular capillaries		11				
vasa recta	16a	12				
cortical radiate vein (blue)		8		17	13 & 14	
arcuate vein	18	7		18	23	
interlobar vein	17				36	
right renal vein	1			1		7
left renal vein						8
inferior vena cava						6

The female urinary system would be identical to the male urinary system model except for the following:

1. The spermatic arteries and veins would be ovarian arteries and veins.
2. The prostate gland, seminal vesicles, and ductus deferens would not be present.
3. The bladder would form a neck into the region occupied by the prostate, with the urethra passing directly from the bladder through the urogenital diaphragm.
4. The uterus would rest on and be attached to the superior surface of the bladder. The peritoneum would only contact the anterior most superior surface. Hysterectomies always traumatize the bladder.

II. MICROSCOPIC ANATOMY OF THE URINARY SYSTEM

Introduction

The functional unit of the kidney, the nephron, is a microscopic structure. The nephron begins with the renal corpuscle. The **renal corpuscles** look like little round islands of cells. The term renal corpuscle means "little body of the kidney" and is a histological term held over from the early days of tissue study before they knew the functions of each part of the kidney. Now we know that the renal corpuscle actually consists of the **glomerulus** (a tuft of capillaries) and the **glomerular (Bowman's) capsule**. The capillaries of the glomerulus are made of simple squamous epithelium. The glomerular capsule is comprised of two layers of simple squamous epithelium with a space between them, the **capsular space**. The visceral layer of the capsule is in contact with the glomerulus. The cells of the visceral layer are called **podocytes**. The parietal layer forms the outer wall of the capsule.

The tubules of the nephron are formed by a single layer of epithelial cells. The type of epithelium varies throughout the tubules. A simple cuboidal epithelium with a brush border of microvilli that increases surface area is found in the **proximal convoluted tubules**. The simple cuboidal transitions to a simple squamous epithelium in the **descending loop of Henle**. The **ascending loop of Henle** transitions from a simple cuboidal to a low columnar. Simple cuboidal epithelium is the tissue type in the **distal convoluted tubules** and the **collecting duct**.

Every nephron has a structure called the juxtaglomerular apparatus, a structure where the afferent arteriole makes contact with the ascending limb of loop of Henle. (Figure 2) Each **juxtaglomerular apparatus** is a combination of a **macula densa**, a thickened part of the ascending loop of Henle and the **juxtaglomerular cells**, which are modified smooth muscle cells in the wall of the afferent arteriole. The macula densa of each nephron monitors the sodium chloride content of the filtrate in the tubules. The juxtaglomerular cells are in a position to monitor the sodium chloride content of the blood as well as blood pressure. Thus the juxtaglomerular apparatus can compare the sodium chloride content of the filtrate to that of the blood and determine whether the nephron needs to retain more or less sodium. Retaining more NaCl causes retention of additional fluid in turn increasing blood volume. An increase in blood volume can raise blood pressure.

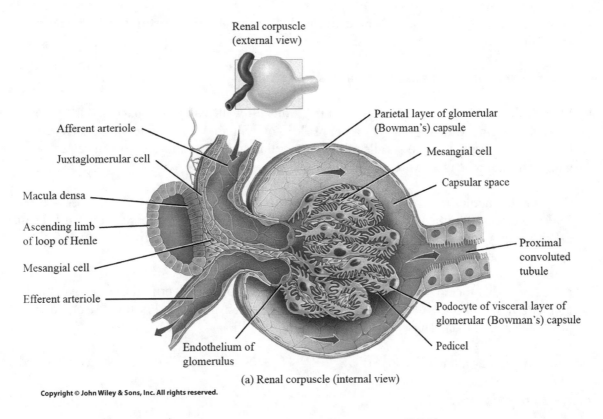

(a) Renal corpuscle (internal view)

Figure 2. The renal corpuscle with the juxtaglomerular apparatus (JGA).

The ureters are long tubes that extend from the kidneys to the urinary bladder. Histologically, the ureters consist of three layers; the mucosa, the muscularis, and the adventitia. The **muscosa** is made of a **transitional epithelium** and its **lamina propria**. There are two layers, an inner longitudinal and an outer circular layer, of smooth muscle in the muscularis. The **adventitia** is an areolar connective tissue.

The histology of the urinary bladder is very similar to the ureters. Transitional epithelium continues within the bladder. The muscularis, also known as the **detrusor muscle**, will add an additional outer longitudinal layer of smooth muscle. The superior surface of the bladder has a serosal layer from the visceral peritoneum.

The epithelium in the urethra begins as transitional epithelium and then transitions to a nonkeratinized squamous epithelium as it nears the skin. The urethra continues to have a muscularis and adventitia layer.

Procedure

Kidney slide

1. Obtain a slide labelled **"Kidney, Human, c.s."**

2. Observe the slide under scanning objective and identify the **renal capsule**, **renal cortex** and **renal medulla**.

3. Focus on the cortex. This can be identified by looking for the **renal corpuscles**.

4. Identify the parts of the renal corpuscle; the **glomerulus**, the **capsular space** and the **parietal layer of the Bowman's (glomerular) capsule**. You will not be able to tell the difference between the simple squamous cells of the glomerulus and the podocytes, so you can call that whole structure the glomerulus.

5. Observe the tubules near the corpuscle. Find a **proximal convoluted tubule** in cross section. This is a circle composed of large cuboidal epithelial cells with lots of pink cytoplasm. These cells contain microvilli which extend into the lumen of the tubule and give it a "fuzzy" appearance.

6. Next find a **distal convoluted tubule** in cross section. You can identify these as the cuboidal epithelium that forms circles with smaller cells with less cytoplasm. For this reason, these tubules appear darker. These cells do not have microvilli.

7. Draw the kidney in the POST-LAB OBSERVATIONS section and label the structures listed.

Juxtaglomerular apparatus

1. Observe the **juxtaglomerular apparatus** on the demonstration scope.

2. Draw the juxtaglomerular apparatus in the POST-LAB OBSERVATIONS section and label the structures listed.

Ureter slide

1. Obtain a slide labeled **"Ureter, Human, cs."**

2. Observe the ureter under scanning and low power. There are three layers. The inner layer around the lumen is called the **mucosa** and is composed of **transitional epithelium** with some mucous secreting cells and a rather thick **lamina propria** of areolar connective tissue. The lamina propria contains networks of elastic fibers that attach the transitional epithelium to the muscularis. The middle layer is called the **muscularis** and is composed of involuntary smooth muscle with inner **longitudinal** and outer **circular layers.** On low power, distinguish the two sets of muscles. The outer layer of the ureter is an **adventitia (fibrous coat)** of connective tissue anchoring the ureter to nearby structures.

3. Observe the mucosa of the ureter under high power. Note the shape of the transitional epithelial cells. Can you observe any mucous secreting cells?

4. Make a sketch of the ureter in the POST-LAB OBSERVATIONS section and label the structures listed.

Urinary System Microscopic Structures

Structure Name - Kidney
renal capsule
renal cortex
renal medulla
renal corpuscle
glomerulus
capsular space
parietal layer of Bowman's (glomerular) capsule
proximal convoluted tubule
distal convoluted tubule
macula densa
Structure Name - Ureter
mucosa
transitional epithelium
lamina propria
longitudinal layer of muscularis
circular layer of muscularis
adventitia (fibrous coat)

III. INTRODUCTION TO KIDNEY FUNCTION USING PHYSIOEX 8.0

Introduction

In this exercise you are going to get an introduction to nephron function using a computer lab simulation program. In the renal corpuscle, blood plasma is pushed from the glomerular capillaries into the capsular space. This process is called **filtration** and it is dependent upon a balance of pressures within the renal corpuscle. When the **net filtration pressure** is high, a sizeable amount of fluid will be pushed into the capsule in a short period of time. The amount of fluid entering the capsular space in a period of time is the **glomerular filtration rate (GFR)**. The net filtration pressure is higher in the glomerulus than in a standard capillary bed, because the arteriole entering the capillary bed, the afferent arteriole, is usually much larger than the arteriole leaving, the efferent arteriole. You are going to explore how changing the size of the afferent and efferent arterioles will change the net filtration pressure, glomerular filtration rate and ultimately the urine production of the nephron. In addition you will explore how changing the initial "blood" pressure of the fluids entering the nephron also affects nephron function.

Procedure

Initial Preparation

1. Proceed as a group to the computer assigned to you.

2. Open PhysioEx 8.0. You do not need to click on site requirements. Just click **Enter**.

3. If your computer prompts you to allow blocked content, always allow blocked content.

4. Choose Exercise 9. Renal System Physiology at top of page with the down arrow. Click **Go**.

5. Click on **Simulating Glomerular Filtration**.

The yellow system of "pipes" on the right represents the nephron filter unit of the kidney. The expanded area is Bowman's capsule. The "pipes" inside the capsule represent the capillary bed called the glomerulus. Above it are areas that record glomerular pressure and glomerular filtration rate (GFR). Urine volume is also displayed.

Exercise I. Changing the radius of the Afferent arteriole:

1. Under Data Sets: click on **Afferent**.

2. Set afferent radius to 0.40 and efferent radius to 0.40.

3. Keep pressure at 90 mmHg in the container that sits above start. This is termed Beaker Pressure and represents the blood pressure of the body. Set concentration Gradient to 1200 (mosm) and do not change it.

4. Hit **Start**. Observe the flow of "blood" into and out of the glomerulus. When run is complete, hit **Record Data**.

5. Now, change the afferent radius to 0.50. Keep all other values constant.

6. Hit **Refill** and then **Start**. After blood flow is complete, hit **Record Data**.

7. Repeat with afferent radius at 0.60. Hit **Refill** and **Start**. Again, **Record Data**.

8. Observe the data and answer the questions in the POST-LAB OBSERVATION section.

9. Predict the effect of constricting the afferent arteriole to 0.30, record your prediction in the POST-LAB OBSERVATION section, and try it in PhysioEx.

Exercise II. Changing the radius of the Efferent Arteriole

1. Keeping the data sets on **Afferent**, set the afferent arteriole radius back to 0.40. Run again with the efferent radius at 0.40 by hitting **Refill** and **Start**. When run is complete, **Record Data**.

2. Now, increase the efferent radius to 0.50. Hit **Refill** and **Start**. Again **Record Data**.

3. Now, set efferent radius to 0.60. Hit **Refill** and **Start**. **Record Data**.

4. Predict the effect of reducing the radius of the efferent arteriole to 0.30, record your prediction in the POST-LAB OBSERVATION section, and try it in PhysioEx.

Exercise III. Effect of systemic blood pressure on glomerular pressure and GFR

1. On Data Sets, set to Combined. Don't worry, your previous data is still saved; you just can't see it at this time. Set afferent radius to 0.40 and efferent radius also to 0.40. Leave beaker pressure at 90 and hit **Refill** and **Start**. **Record data**.

2. Now change only Beaker pressure to 80. Hit **Refill** and **Start**. After run, **Record data**.

3. Click **Tools** → **Print Data** at the top of the page to print your data.

4. Observe the data and answer the questions in the POST-LAB OBSERVATION section.

5. Do some more runs with beaker pressure at 80 and change your afferent and efferent arteriole diameters to the values you predict in the Clinical Thinking question to see if you are correct.

PRE-LAB QUESTIONS   **Name**_____

Answer by reading the lab manual before coming to lab!

A. List in order the structures of the nephron and the kidney tubule system that urine passes
    through from its site of formation as filtrate to the renal pelvis.

    _____   _____

    _____   _____

    _____   _____

    _____   _____

    _____   _____

B. What two structures make up the juxtaglomerular apparatus?

    _____ and _____

C. List in order the vessels the blood flows through from the renal artery to the renal vein

    _____   _____

    _____   _____

    _____   _____

    _____   _____

    _____   _____

    _____

D. What is the usual blood pressure in the glomerulus? _____

    1. How does this compare with the pressure in other capillary beds?

E. What are the vasa recta?

F. List the functions of the kidney.

G. From the History: What is the other name for the glomerular capsule?

    1. Who is it named after? _____

III. INTRODUCTION TO KIDNEY FUNCTION USING PHYSIOEX 8.0

Exercise I. Changing the radius of the Afferent arteriole:

1. Dilating the afferent arteriole increases blood flow into the glomerulus. What effect does this have on:

   Glomerular pressure   _____

   GFR   _____

   Urine volume   _____

2. What do you predict will happen if you constrict the afferent arteriole to 0.30?

   _____

   a. Did the data match your prediction? _____

Exercise II. Changing the radius of the Efferent Arteriole

3. Dilating the efferent arteriole decreases resistance to the flow of blood in the glomerular capillaries, thus decreasing the pressure. What does this do to:

   Glomerular pressure   _____

   GFR   _____

   Urine volume   _____

4. What happened to urine volume and GFR when the efferent radius was set at 0.60?

   _____

   a. Why do you think this happened? _____

5. What do you think would happen if you reduced the radius of the efferent arteriole to 0.30?

   _____

   a. Did the data match your prediction? _____

Exercise III. Effect of systemic blood pressure on glomerular pressure and GFR

1. What affect does reducing the beaker pressure have on:

   Glomerular pressure   _____

   GFR   _____

   Urine volume   _____

Remember, Beaker pressure here represents systemic blood pressure.

2. Clinical Thinking: What do you think would happen in a patient who is going into shock?

     a. What would the kidneys try to do to the afferent and efferent arterioles to overcome the effects of shock and try to continue to make urine?

        Would they constrict or dilate the afferent arteriole? _____

        Would they constrict or dilate the efferent arteriole? _____

URINALYSIS

HISTORY

Throughout the Middle Ages, physicians diagnosed many diseases by the spurious "science" of urinoscopy. This procedure owes its origin to Isaac Judeus, an Egyptian doctor, who lived from 845 to 940 A.D. He recommended that the urine be studied by looking at it when held up to the light. (There were no microscopes at this time.) It was observed for its color, density and shape of clouds that formed in it. He recognized four levels in the flask of urine, each corresponding to a part of the body. If the cloudiness was at the top, the head was the seat of the disease, and so on down to the bottom of the flask which represented the legs and feet. His works were printed in 1515 and remained popular for more than one hundred years. During this time, patients would go to their doctors with their samples in glass vials carried in special wicker baskets.

OBJECTIVES

1. To perform various chemical tests on your own urine.
2. To perform tests and analyze data from some abnormal constituents which may be present in urine.
3. To inspect your urine microscopically for sediments

I. CHEMICAL ANALYSIS OF URINE SPECIMENS

Introduction

Urine contains a rather comprehensive biochemical profile of a body's metabolism. Analysis of urine is an important tool to determine normal function and check for pathologies. Urine quality and quantity vary over a 24 hour period reflecting our changing metabolism, fluid intake and diet. Amino acids, the results of protein digestion, have the nitrogen removed (deamination) prior to storage as fat. This nitrogen will convert to ammonia unless the liver can convert it to the less toxic urea. Uric acid is formed from the metabolism of nucleic acids. Tests on more than a single specimen may be required in a clinical setting when attempting a diagnosis. Fortunately for us, many of the common tests have been highly refined so that the actual procedures for their performance are quite simple.

Collection of Urine Specimen

Before you can analyze your urine you must collect it. Freshly voided urine is relatively clean if not sterile, so no special cautions are in order if handling only your own specimen. To minimize contamination with extraneous bacteria, skin cells or other debris, you should obtain a **mid-stream sample**.

Appearance of Urine

The color of urine varies from a dark amber color to clear with just a tinge of yellow. Freshly voided urine is usually transparent but may become cloudy upon standing due to the multiplication of bacteria. Urine is colored by the pigment **urochrome** as well as some drugs, blood, and bile pigments. The presence of phosphates or pus is the usual cause of cloudiness in a fresh specimen. Pus in the urine results from urinary tract infections and is called **pyuria**.

Multistix Tests

Ten different chemical tests are combined on each of these strips. Each little square is like a miniature analytical chemistry lab! A number of reagents including a color indicator are combined in each little pad of paper to react specifically with eight different substances which may be present in urine. Normally, none of these eight substances are present and so their presence may indicate disease. In addition, there are two strips that measure pH and specific gravity which may turn colors, but not indicate disease as these can vary due to other causes.

In order from the tab that you hold and time that test should be read, these tests are:

Glucose in the urine is termed **glycosuria**. Glycosuria is caused by diabetes mellitus or other conditions which elevate the blood sugar level. Normally, as the kidney is filtering the blood and processing the filtrate it recovers all the glucose, amino acids, and other useful substances so that none of these is found in the urine. However, when the concentration of a substance exceeds the kidney's reabsorbing capacity it will pass with the urine.

Bilirubin is a bile pigment which is a breakdown product of hemoglobin. Bilirubin circulates in the blood bound to albumin and is extracted by the liver to be stored in the gall bladder as bile. Bile is released from the gall bladder into the duodenum in response to the presence of fats. Bile also contains bile salts which emulsify fat. Liver damage due to chemicals such as cleaning agents or alcohol may result in bilirubin being present in the urine.

Ketones, such as acetone, are toxic substances normally produced in small quantities and are quickly altered by the liver. Excessive ketone production results from catabolism (breakdown) of large quantities of fats for energy and produces the condition **ketosis**. Ketosis is commonly associated with diabetes mellitus.

Specific gravity of urine is a measure of the solute content of the sample. It can be measured with a multistix. It can also be measured with a urinometer as described below. Increased fluid intake will lower specific gravity, dehydration and solutes in the urine will raise it.

Blood cells and the large plasma proteins are too large to pass through the healthy membrane filters of the kidney. Thus the presence of these substances in a specimen usually indicates disease. Hemorrhaging may be from the urethra, bladder, ureters, or kidneys depending on the site of infection. Disease may not be the only cause, however, as during a female's menses, blood from the vagina may contaminate a urine specimen.

pH is the measure of the hydrogen ion concentration. Normally the blood pH is 7.40. The body is able to maintain this slightly alkaline pH through an elaborate system of buffers and the kidney's selective excretion of excess acids or bases. The pH of urine may range from 4 to 8 but is usually about 6. The foods we eat can influence the pH of urine. Protein in foods such as meat generates acid. Vegetables generate base and make the urine more alkaline.

Upon voiding, bacteria are introduced into the urine specimen. Bacteria use the urea in urine for nutrition converting it to alkaline ammonia. Thus, urine that has been left to stand is usually alkaline. Bacterial action and the resulting ammonia also gives old urine its characteristic odor.

Protein in the urine is termed **proteinuria**. A slight amount of proteinuria is normally present in only 5% of the population. Its abnormal presence is associated with such conditions as renal diseases, pregnancy or hypertension.

Urobilinogen is formed when bacteria reduce bilirubin (a breakdown product of hemoglobin) to urobilinogen in the intestines. Bilirubin is released into the intestines by the liver in the bile. Normally urobilinogen is not found in the urine. Depression of the excretory function of the liver by disease or poisons such as cleaning agents may cause urobilinogen to appear.

Nitrites may appear if gram negative bacteria convert nitrates present in food to the nitrite form. The test for nitrites is thus more important as an indicator of bacteria than of the presence of the chemical itself. *Escherichia coli*, common in the colon, and *Salmonella sp.* are two types of gram negative bacteria. The presence of bacteria in the urine is termed **bacteriuria.**

Leucocytes are white blood cells. Their presence is an indication of a urinary tract infection. These infections are more common in women than in men due in part to the shorter urethra.

Specific Gravity

Specific gravity expresses the weight of a substance relative to the weight of an equal volume of water. If a substance is less dense than water its specific gravity will be some value less than one. A substance more dense than water will have a specific gravity greater than one. Adding solutes to water typically increases the specific gravity of the solution. Normal specific gravity values for urine obtained over a 24 hour period range from 1.016 to 1.022. High fluid intake normally results in a specific gravity reading for a single specimen closer to 1.000.

The specific gravity of a urine specimen is a product of the kidney's effort to maintain homeostasis. When fluid intake is insufficient to counter balance fluid losses an individual tends to become dehydrated. The kidneys retain as much water as possible and in the process produce urine that is more concentrated with solutes. This increases the specific gravity of the specimen. Some other factors which would contribute to increased specific gravity are **diabetes mellitus**, (which results in glucose in the urine) acute glomerulonephritis (inflammation of the kidneys filtering membranes), a drop in blood pressure, pain and emotional stress.

On the other hand, drinking lots of fluids should increase urine production. This larger urine output would be of lower specific gravity. Increased blood pressure, cold stress, alcohol consumption, epinephrine, and **diabetes insipidus** (which results in urine with a high water content) are all conditions which contribute to a reduced specific gravity of urine. Diabetes insipidus is a condition that results from insufficient secretion of anti-diuretic hormone (ADH) from the posterior pituitary gland. With lower ADH levels, the kidney nephrons reabsorb less water from the collecting ducts, resulting in a greater quantity of more dilute urine.

The routine clinical specimen is collected in the morning after fasting. Random samples during the day reflect the person's diet, fluid intake, physical activity, and exposure to heat stress over the previous hour just to mention just a few variables. Thus checking the specific gravity of your specimen would have limited value. Specific gravity can be checked with a Multistix or using an urinometer. The **urinometer** which you will use is a special chamber and a **hydrometer** (float) calibrated to read specific gravity to the nearest 0.001 at 15°C. If the temperature of the urine deviates from 15°C, a correction factor must be calculated.

Procedure

Collection of Urine Specimen

1. You will collect and analyze your own urine. You are to work with ONLY your own specimen.

2. Collect the urine specimen in a clean container that will be provided to you. Move the foreskin or labia away from the urethral orifice and urinate several milliliters of urine into the toilet before collecting your sample (at least 10 ml) by urinating into the cup.

Remember that freshly voided urine is relatively clean if not sterile, so no special cautions are in order if handling only your own specimen. Never-the-less, it is always a good procedure to UTILIZE SANITARY PRACTICES and wash your hands after handling your genitals. If you were handling another person's urine, wearing latex gloves would be appropriate, but you certainly do NOT need them when working with just your own specimen. Please wash any lab equipment your urine comes in contact with during the following procedures.

Appearance of Urine

1. Record the color and transparency of your specimen in the POST-LAB OBSERVATION section.

If the urine is cloudy, this could be due either to crystalline substances in the urine or pus. If it is due to crystals, you will be able to observe them under the microscope. If it is pus, you will observe the white blood cells which make up pus.

Multistix Tests

Multistixs are expensive, over $1 each. Please use only one strip with your specimen. DO NOT touch the reagent area of a Multistix. Remember that most of the tests of your urine should yield negative results.

1. Remove a strip from the bottle and immediately replace the cap securely. Room air causes the strips to deteriorate.

2. Dip the strip in the urine and remove immediately. Note the time!

3. Tap the edge of the strip against the urine container to remove excess fluid. Work over a paper towel and blot on it if necessary.

4. Hold the strip horizontally to minimize mixing of the various reagents on the strip.

5. Compare the color on the strip to the color charts on the bottle starting with the glucose square (the square closest to the tab). Be sure and watch the time as these must be timed!

6. Record your results in the POST-LAB OBSERVATION section. Use a "-" for negative, and a "+" for a trace, a "++" for moderate, and "+++" for large amounts.

7. When you are done with your Multistix, dispose of it in the Biohazard trash.

8. Save your urine for the microscopic examination of urine.

II. CHEMICAL ANALYSIS OF ARTIFICAL URINE SAMPLES

Introduction

You will also test "pathological" urine samples from several "patients" which allows you to observe the presence of abnormal constituents. These specimens were actually created by the lab technician, NOT someone's kidneys and do NOT contain pathogenic organisms. Precautions are NOT required when working with these samples.

Procedure

Multistix Tests

1. Each table should work as a group to test the "pathological" urine specimens.

2. Remove enough strips from the bottle to test all the samples and immediately replace the cap securely. Room air causes the strips to deteriorate.

3. Dip one strip into each of the urine samples and remove immediately. Note the time!

4. Tap the edge of the strip against the urine container to remove excess fluid.

5. Take the Multistix(s) to your workspace and work over a paper towel and blot on it if necessary.

6. Hold the strip horizontally to minimize mixing of the various reagents on the strip.
7. Compare the color on the strip to the color charts on the bottle starting with the glucose square (the square closest to the tab). Be sure and watch the time as these must be timed!

8. Record your results for each sample in the POST-LAB OBSERVATION section. Use a "-" for negative, and a "+" for a trace, a "++" for moderate, and "+++" for large amounts.

9. Match the "patients" described to the "pathological" urine samples.

10. When you are done with your Multistix(s), dispose of it/them in the Biohazard trash.

Specific Gravity

You will only need to perform the procedure below using the urinometer on the two demonstration specimens labeled F and G. The urinometers marked "Patients" F and G have been filled to within about one inch of the top with "pathological" urine. The hydrometer was gently floated in the urine.

1. Give the top a slight twirl so it floats freely.

2. Record the reading at the point where the liquid hits the scale. (This is termed the meniscus.)

3. Measure the temperature of the specimen. Add 0.001 to your hydrometer reading for each three degrees the temperature exceeds 15°C. If below 15°C you would subtract rather than add.

4. Record corrected specific gravity reading in the POST-LAB OBSERVATION section.

III. MICROSCOPIC EXAMINATION OF URINE

Introduction

Microscopic examination of urine is a crucial component of urine analysis. A complete microscopic examination includes analysis of sediments and identification of any bacteria present. In healthy people the kidneys, ureters, and bladder are free of microorganisms. The lower third of the male urethra has a resident microbial population. These microbes compete for existing resources and reduce the possibility of successful colonization by potentially dangerous pathogens. The female urethra is usually sterile, if she drinks plenty of fluids to frequently wash it with urine. However, her urethra can easily become infected due to the warm moist habitat near the opening, ideal for bacterial growth, and its proximity to the anus. This infection may then spread to the bladder and kidneys. If pathogens enter the blood of either a male or female, they may be able to establish themselves in the kidney. For example, the streptococcus of a strep throat infection, perhaps asymptomatic, may establish in the heart or kidneys with serious effects.

Microscopic examination of the urine offers many valuable clues in the detection and evaluation of urinary tract disorders. The importance of urinary tract infections and their effect on kidney functions cannot be over emphasized. Untreated they can lead to permanent impairment of kidney function, renal insufficiency and hypertension. Urine sediments are not only useful diagnostic tools for infections; they also provide insight into normal kidney function.

We have a collection of photographic slides of sediments that can be found in urine. You should be able to identify all the bold faced examples from a photographic slide.

A **cast** results from solidification of matter in the nephrons. Usually the casts are cemented together by albumin which has leaked into the tubule from the blood. Casts may contain only protein and are thus called hyaline casts. They may also contain various cells and are called cell casts. After formation, urine subsequently washes the cast downstream. Examining casts may be as effective as a tissue biopsy in revealing pathological problems. Some casts that you may see in your sample include:

a. **Hyaline casts** are composed chiefly of protein with no inclusions.
b. White blood **cell casts** may be present if an infection is present but are rare. They are easily confused with epithelial casts.
c. **Red blood cell casts** may indicate damage or disease.
d. **Epithelial cell casts** contain cells that have sloughed off from the tubules or urinary bladder.
e. **Broad casts** are large because they form in the larger collecting tubules. If present in quantity, they block the kidney tubules impairing renal function.

Normal urine will contain **cells** including an occasional leukocyte and some epithelial cells. The **epithelial cells** are usually squamous cells from the bladder and urethra. In females, squamous cells from the vagina may contaminate the sample. Cuboidal epithelial cells derived from the kidney tubules are difficult to distinguish from the transitional cells of the bladder. Excess sloughing off of epithelial cells indicates pathology and recognizing the cell type helps the physician locate the problem. Bacterial cells and yeast cells may indicate infection. Some cells that you may see in your sample include:

a. Epithelial cells: These cells may be found in small amounts in urine sediment of normal urine.
   1) Tubular cells as the name implies are from the nephron tubules. They are somewhat larger than leukocytes and may appear cuboidal in form or be columnar.
   2) **Transitional epithelial cells** are quite large and tend to be spindle shaped or pear shaped. They come from the renal pelvis as well as the bladder and ureters.
   3) **Squamous epithelial cells** are large, typically flat irregular cells. They are native to the urethra and the vagina, and unless associated with excess bacteria are of little importance.
b. **White blood cells** may be present if an infection of the genito-urinary tract is present. If present, they are crenated due to the hypertonic urine. They are not normally found in the urine.
c. **Red blood** cells: Generally these are not found in normal urine. When present, they usually represent injury to the glomerular membrane as happens with infections and in long distance runners. RBCs may represent contamination with menstrual flow at the time of collection. Red blood cells will be crenated (shriveled).

Many **crystals** may be found in urine depending to some degree on diet, the person's physiology, and the pH of the urine. Common ones found in normal urine are calcium oxylate from vegetable intake and uric acid from protein intake. Some crystals that you may see in your sample include:

a. **Calcium oxalate**, small crystals which appear in two principal forms -octahedral and dumbbell. Excessive ingestion of spinach, tomatoes, garlic, oranges and asparagus will increase the amount found in the urine. Calcium oxalate mixed with phosphate salt is found in renal calculi (kidney stones) and is their principal ingredient.
b. Calcium phosphate, small crystals which appear as feathery crystals and as prisms. They are usually present in small amounts in alkaline urine. One interesting form is called the **"coffin lid" form of phosphate.**
c. Uric acid, these crystals may be present in a variety of forms, small square rhombic prisms and as sheaves and rosettes. One common form is shaped like a football and appears shiny like a mirror. This often indicates protein intake and is not pathological.
d. Hippuric acid, less common in urine, they stain brown and appear as long rod shaped structures or in stellate form.
e. Tyrosine and leucine amino acid crystals usually appear in the urine together as fine needles in star burst form. Neither are normal constituents, unless they are due to excessive nutritional intake.
f. Cholesterol crystals may be found in urine. An interesting form is the **"Maltese Cross" form of cholesterol.** Presence of this indicates disease.

In addition, certain **non-bacterial organisms** may be found including those indigenous to the urinary tract as well as some contaminating the urine stream. Four of the more common are described below.

a. The pin worm (*Enterobius vermicularis*) may migrate from the anus to the vaginal areas and be washed into the urine stream. More commonly the small oval ovum will be found.
b. *Trichomonas vaginalis* is the most common parasite in the urine, occurring in approximately 25% of all women. It is a highly motile ovoid organism with multiple flagella extending anteriorly. If the flagella are absent or altered by autolysis it may be mistaken for an epithelial cell.
c. **Sperm** are a normal component of a sexually mature male's urine, unless he has had a vasectomy. Sperm in a female's urine represents another vaginal contaminate.
d. **Yeast** cells are not generally found in urine. There presence may indicate an infection.

A variety of plant fibers, **pollen grains**, dandruff, talcum powder, hairs and other artifacts may be present in a less carefully collected specimen. Your lab instructor will attempt to help you identify these unknowns. They are artifacts of collection and are not associated with pathology.

Procedure

1. Pour or pipette 10 ml of urine into a clean plastic centrifuge tube. Mark the tube with your initials using a wax pencil.

2. Place your tube in the centrifuge head noting its position. Make sure your tube is counter balanced by another tube containing 10 ml of urine or water. Your instructor will centrifuge the samples.

3. Carefully remove your tube to the test tube rack at your desk. From the supply table you need a pipette dropper, 3 microscope slides, marked "2", "1" and "0", a bottle of "Sedi stain" and three cover slips. Work on a paper towel!

4. With the pipette dropper, carefully remove a small drop of concentrated urine from the centrifuge tube 2 cm above the bottom of the tube. To obtain the sample, squeeze the pipette bulb **before** you put it in the sample! You must only squeeze the bulb slightly, maintaining a precise release of pressure on the bulb to draw up just a drop into the tip of the dropper. If you disturb the sediment, you should return the urine to the tube and have the instructor centrifuge your specimen again.

a. Place the sample on the slide marked "2". Add a small drop of Sedi-stain to the urine on the slide. Place a cover slip over the drop.

5. Now, remove a small drop from the level 1 cm above the centrifuge tube bottom, place it on the slide marked "1". Stain as before.

6. Finally repeat the procedures with a drop sample from the very bottom of the tube. Place this sample on the slide marked "0" and stain.

7. Identify as many of the substances in your "2" specimen as possible by comparing to the charts on the wall or to the figures in the provided books. Also use the photographic slides as a guide. If you cannot find it in the book, call the instructor.

8. Note that Sedi-Stain when dry, will form yellow to purple crystals. You may see these crystals near the edge of the cover slip. If you put Sedi-Stain on the slide before the urine sample, there may also be a residual ring of Sedi-Stain crystals where the edge of the Sedi-Stain once was.

9. Draw and list what you see in the POST-LAB OBSERVATION section. If you cannot identify the object, draw it and you can call it a UFO (unidentified floating object!) If you are concerned, take the drawings to your physician!

10. Repeat for the slides marked "1" and "0". The sediments in the urine are of varying densities in the different samples. Centrifugation causes the heaviest sediments to go to the very bottom with less dense particles layered out in zones above. We perform this three step sampling procedure in order to get some idea of the relative density of the urine's sedimentary components as well as their relative abundance in your specimen.

11. Clean the microscope's objectives and stage with isopropyl alcohol to remove any residual Sedi-stain before putting the microscope away.

PRE-LAB QUESTIONS   **Name** _____

I. CHEMICAL ANALYSIS OF URINE SPECIMENS

A. Why do all urine specimens turn cloudy upon standing?

B. What is the normal pH range for urine? _____

C. Why do all urine specimens become alkaline upon standing?

D. How much glucose is normally found in urine? _____

II. CHEMICAL ANALYSIS OF ARTIFICAL URINE SAMPLES

A. What factors increase specific gravity?

B. What factors decrease it?

III. MICROSCOPIC EXAMINATION OF URINE

A. Name some constituents of urine that are contaminates and are not formed in the urinary system.

B. What amino acid crystals might be found in the urine?

C. If WBCs are present in the urine, what would they be the result of?

D. Name 2 types of casts that may be found in the urine.

_____ and _____

E. Where in the urinary system do the transitional epithelial cells originate that are found in the urine?

F. Name 2 non-bacterial organisms that may be found in the urine.

_____ and _____

POST-LAB OBSERVATIONS

I. CHEMICAL ANALYSIS OF URINE SPECIMENS

Appearance of your urine

A. Color _____

B. Transparency _____

C. If your specimen was cloudy, was the cloudy appearance caused by WBCs or crystals or both? (microscopic analysis can determine this!)

Multistix Tests

A. Compare your Multistix to the color scale. Start with the square closest to your fingers and note the time!

glucose _____

bilirubin _____

ketones _____

specific gravity _____

blood _____

pH _____

protein _____

urobilinogen _____

nitrite _____

leukocytes _____

II. CHEMICAL ANALYSIS OF ARTIFICAL URINE SAMPLES

Multistix Tests

A. "Pathological" specimen analysis. Read the Multistix for each specimen and record the results. (Assume these are "fresh" samples, although they sat there a while!)

	Specimen A	Specimen B	Specimen C	Specimen D	Specimen E
Glucose					
Bilirubin					
Ketone					
Specific Gravity					
Blood					
pH					
Protein					
Urobilinogen					
Nitrite					
Leukocytes					

B. "Clinical Thinking" Task. Unfortunately, the samples you have measured above, belonged to the patients below and the names came off the specimen containers! Your task, as a lab group, is to figure out which urine belongs to which patient. Information in the lab on the items measured by the Multistix will help you with your conclusions. Explain each abnormal value! Good luck.

1. **Chris W**. is a Caucasian male, 25 years old, 6 ft 150 lbs. His EKG is normal and he has a hematocrit of 38% and a BP of 128/70. He saw his primary physician complaining of exhaustion. He is an Environmental Studies graduate student and a vegan with no history of cardiovascular disease.

   Which samples is his? _____
   Discuss what led you to this conclusion: (write below)

2. **Maria R.** is a Hispanic female age 60, 5 feet 3 inches, 185 lbs. She has a hematocrit of 42% and a BP of 130/85. She came in complaining of increased fatigue. Her appetite remains excellent, although her thirst has suddenly increased.

    Which sample is hers? _____
    Discuss what led you to this conclusion: (write below)

3. **Anne L.** is an African-American female age 25, 5 feet 5 inches, 120 lbs. She has a hematocrit of 38% and a BP of 185/95. She entered the emergency room complaining of a headache and sudden swelling of her lower extremities

    Which sample is hers? _____
    Discuss what led you to this conclusion: (write below)

4. **Lei T.** is an Asian female, age 55. 5 feet 2 inches, 110 lbs. She has a hematocrit of 40% and a BP of 110/70. After a vacation in her home country, she experienced diarrhea for one week duration. She commented that this was the first time she had missed work due to illness in the 30 years she had worked at her family's dry cleaning establishment. The diarrhea seemed to clear up, but now she experiences discomfort upon urination as well as increased frequency.

    Which sample is hers? _____
    Discuss what led you to this conclusion: (write below)

5. **David H**. is a 45 year old Caucasian male. 6 feet 2, 220 lbs. His hematocrit is 50% and has a BP of 135/75. He saw his personal physician complaining of a swollen abdomen, puffiness in the face and legs and easy bruising. His appearance is very important to him as he is in show business. His recent divorce and the ensuing custody battle over the children has put him under a great deal of stress.

Which sample is his? _____
Discuss what led you to this conclusion: (write below)

Specific Gravity

A. "Pathological" specimen analysis. Read the specific gravity for each specimen and record the results.

	"Patient" F	"Patient" G
Hydrometer reading	_____	_____
Temperature °C	_____	_____
Corrected specific gravity of urine	_____	_____

What is the normal range of specific gravity? _____

Is this value within the normal range?	_____	_____

B. "Clinical Thinking" Task.

A. Paul T. is a Native American who has to check his blood sugar each day to monitor his insulin dose.

Is he patient F or G? _____

B. Jane S. has given birth to her third child. The resulting clot in the blood vessels to the pituitary gland has blocked the release of Anti Diuretic Hormone (ADH).

Is she patient F or G? _____

III. MICROSCOPIC EXAMINATION OF URINE

A. List the substances found in your centrifuged specimen and draw their picture!

   1. 2 cm sample

   2. 1 cm sample

3. 0 cm (bottom) sample

DIGESTIVE SYSTEM ANATOMY

HISTORY

It seems strange at first that a system whose actions include hunger, eating and bowel action would attract so little attention from early medicine. The digestive system was relatively neglected until recent centuries. The exceptions to this are the liver and the gall bladder which were used to predict the future. Although Herophilus, a physician at the medical school at Alexandria in the third century BC, did describe the duodenum whose name means twelve finger breadths and the lacteals, a word derived from milk, it was not until Andreas Vesalius' work *De Humani Corporis Fabrica* in 1543 that digestive anatomy was presented with any semblance of accuracy.

The pancreatic duct long known as Wirsung's duct was described in 1642 by the German anatomist Johann Wirsung who was assassinated in 1643 possibly as a result of a dispute over priority in the discovery of the duct. The intestinal glands were (and sometimes still are) called the crypts of Lieberkühn after a German physician in the 1700s even though they were actually described by Malpighi in 1688. The ampulla of Vater was described by another German, Abraham Vater, professor of Anatomy at the University of Wittenberg. The sphincter of Oddi was named after Ruggero Oddi, an Italian physician although he was not the first to describe it. These now have the new names of the "hepatopancreatic ampulla" and the "sphincter of the hepatopancreatic ampulla" respectively. It is not surprising that the eponyms are often still used.

OBJECTIVES

1. To learn the gross anatomy of the organs comprising the digestive system.
2. To learn the histology of the organs comprising the digestive system.
3. To get an introduction to digestive physiology using a computer lab simulation program.

I. GROSS ANATOMY OF THE DIGESTIVE SYSTEM

Introduction

The digestive system includes the **gastrointestinal tract (GI tract, alimentary canal, "gut")** and associated structures. In vertebrates the GI tract is about 30 feet long and consists of the mouth, pharynx, esophagus, stomach, small intestine, large intestine, and anus. Each of these may include several structures or distinct subdivisions. For example, the duodenum, jejunum and ileum are parts of the small intestine. The cecum, ascending, transverse, descending, sigmoid colon and rectum are parts of the large intestine. The accessory organs involved in digestion are the teeth, salivary glands, liver, and pancreas.

Digestion begins when food is ingested in the **mouth (oral or buccal cavity)**. The mouth is bounded on the lateral sides by the cheeks, to the superior by the **hard and soft palates**, to the anterior by the lips, and to the inferior by the **tongue**.

Within the mouth are the **teeth**. The parts of a tooth are the **crown**, the part of the tooth that we see; the **neck**, the part of the tooth at the gum line; the **root**, the part that is attached to the mandible or maxilla by the **periodontal ligament**; and the **pulp cavity**, the interior of a tooth that contains blood vessels and nerves. **Enamel**, a very hard substance, covers the crown. The main body of the tooth is made of **dentin**. The periodontal ligament attaches to the root through a substance called **cementum**. The nerves within the pulp cavity are branches of the trigeminal nerve (V). Humans will have two sets of teeth, 20 **deciduous (primary) teeth** and 32 **permanent (secondary) teeth**. There are four different types of teeth: **incisors, canines (cuspids), bicuspids (premolars)**, and **molars**. An adult should have eight incisors, four **central incisors** and four **lateral incisors**. The incisors are used for cutting food. Four canines are used for tearing food. There are a total of eight bicuspids and twelve molars. They are used for grinding food. The molars are divided into four **first molars**, four **second molars** and four **third molars (wisdom teeth)**.

The salivary glands are accessory structures that empty into the mouth. Their function is to make **saliva**. One of the components of saliva is **salivary amylase**, an enzyme that breaks down starch. Humans have three pairs of salivary glands. The **parotid salivary glands** are located near the ears, the **submandibular (submaxillary) salivary glands** are under the chin and the **sublingual salivary glands** are under the tongue.

The mouth is connected to the **pharynx** by the **fauces**. Food will travel from the mouth to the pharynx, through the esophagus, to the stomach. The **esophagus** penetrates the diaphragm through the esophageal hiatus. The circular layer of smooth muscle in the lower end of the esophagus and adjacent part of the stomach is called the **lower esophageal sphincter**. It was formerly called the cardiac sphincter, as when the stomach is too full or the sphincter too weak, the contents of the stomach rise into the esophagus causing "heartburn". Although the name of the sphincter has changed, the portion of the stomach near it is still called the cardia.

The **stomach** is a J-shaped enlargement of the GI tract that begins at the end of the esophagus and ends at the pyloric sphincter. The shorter, superior curve of the stomach is called the **lesser curvature** and the longer, inferior curve is called the **greater curvature**. The regions of the stomach are the **cardia**, the entrance area of the stomach inferior to the heart; the **fundus**, the superior portion of the stomach that forms a dome structure; the **body**, the large middle section of the stomach; and the **pylorus**, the narrower section of the stomach that ends at the pyloric sphincter. The **pyloric sphincter** is a band of smooth muscle that controls the movement of material out of the stomach. The inner lining of the stomach has stretchable folds called **rugae**. Protein digestion begins in the stomach, but the stomach has a limited ability to digest carbohydrates.

The **pancreas** is just inferior to the stomach. Anatomically, the pancreas is divided into the head, the body, and tail. Running the length of the pancreas is the **pancreatic duct (duct of Wirsung)**, which enters the duodenum at the **hepatopancreatic ampulla (ampulla of Vater)** within the major **duodenal papilla**. The **accessory pancreatic duct (duct of Santorini)** is a shorter duct with a separate opening into the duodenum. The pancreas produces a pancreatic juice containing bicarbonate ions that neutralize the pH of the contents coming from the stomach and many enzymes that aid in digestion of proteins, lipids, carbohydrates and nucleic acids.

The **liver** is the large organ located inferior to the diaphragm. It is divisible into left and right lobes which are separated by the **falciform ligament**. The liver produces bile, which aids in the digestion of lipids. The **gallbladder** is a sac located in a depression on the inferior surface of the liver that stores bile until it is needed by the duodenum. The bile is conducted to the duodenum through a system of ducts. The **hepatic ducts** (right hepatic duct, left hepatic duct and common hepatic duct) merge with the **cystic duct** (bile duct from the gallbladder) to become the **common bile duct**. The common bile duct enters the duodenum at the hepatopancreatic ampulla (ampulla of Vater) after it unites with the pancreatic duct.

The **small intestine** is the longest section of the GI tract. It is divided into three sections. The first section is the **duodenum**, which is about 10 inches long. Next is the **jejunum**, which is about 8 feet long. The last section is the **ileum**, which is about 12 feet long. A muscular valve called the **ileocecal valve (sphincter)** guards the exit from the small intestine. The main functions of the small intestines are to complete the digestion of ingested food and to absorb the nutrients into the body.

The last section of the GI tract is the **large intestine (colon)**, which extends from the ileocecal sphincter to the anus. The large intestine is subdivided into many sections. The **cecum** is a blind pouch inferior to the iliocecal sphincter, and the **appendix** is a structure that hangs inferior to the cecum. Next is the **ascending colon**. The ascending colon will turn medially inferior to the liver at the **right colic (hepatic) flexure** and continue to the **transverse colon**. The transverse colon turns inferiorly inferior to the spleen at the **left colic (splenic) flexure** and continues to the **descending colon**. Next is the **sigmoid colon**. The **rectum** is the section that runs straight up and down. The last section is the **anal canal** and **anus**. Running the length of the large intestines is the **taenia coli (pl. taeniae coli)** a longitudinal "line" of muscle that is found along the length of the large intestine. The taenia coli gathers the large intestine into a series of pouches called the **haustra (s. haustrum)**. The main function of the large intestines is to eliminate non-digestible wastes.

The organs of the digestive system show specializations for distinct diets. For instance, the large intestine is shorter in carnivores due to their diet being almost devoid of dietary fiber. They also have no appendix. The cecum of deer and horses is large to harbor bacteria that digest cellulose. Our teeth, as well as the length of our digestive tract assure that we are omnivores.

The purpose of our digestive system is to obtain food, physically break it down into particles, and then chemically digest the particles into molecules small enough to be absorbed into the circulatory system. Keep these functions in mind as you examine the gross and microscopic structures of the digestive system.

Procedure

The human digestive system will be studied using a variety of models in lab. Refer to the textbook when studying and learn the structures, not the numbers! You are responsible for the following structures even when not numbered on the models! Structures grayed out in the table are not shown on that model.

Structure Name	Teeth Plaque	Digestive System Plaque	Digestive System Model (white base)	Digestive System Model (green base)	Pancreas with Duodenum and Spleen	Torso Model
mouth/oral cavity		1				
maxillary teeth	A	2	1			
mandibular teeth	B	2	1			
central incisors	1					
lateral incisors	2					
cuspids or canines	3					
first premolars (bicuspids)	4					
second premolars (bicuspids)	5					
first molars	6					
second molars	7					
third molars (wisdom teeth)	8					
hard palate	10		3	1		260
raphe	11					
soft palate	12		4	2		
uvula	13		4a	2a		261
alveolar nerve	14					
alveolar artery	15					
alveolar vein	16					
crown	17					
neck	17a					
root	18					
enamel	19					
dentin	20					
pulp cavity	21					
root canal	22					
cementum	23					
apical foramen	24					
gingiva	25					
periodontal ligament	26					
alveolar bone of mandible	28					

Structure Name	Teeth Plaque	Digestive System Plaque	Digestive System Model (white base)	Digestive System Model (green base)	Pancreas with Duodenum and Spleen	Torso Model
tongue		3	2	3		247
parotid salivary gland		4				119
submandibular salivary glands		5				120
sublingual salivary glands		5				
fauces			5			
pharynx		6		4		246
esophagus		7	6	5		136
esophageal (cardiac) sphincter of stomach			7g			
stomach		8	7	6		167
cardia of stomach			7a	6a		168
body of stomach			7			173
fundus of stomach		25	7b	6b		172
pylorus of stomach						174
greater curvature of stomach			7d			171
lesser curvature of stomach			7c			170
serosa		29				
longitudinal muscle layer		26				
circular muscle layer		27				
oblique muscle layer		28				
rugae		30	7f	6e		
pyloric sphincter		31	7e	6f		169

Structure Name	Teeth Plaque	Digestive System Plaque	Digestive System Model (white base)	Digestive System Model (green base)	Pancreas with Duodenum and Spleen	Torso Model
small intestine			13	14		175
duodenum		11	8	7	C	176
duodenal papilla					4	
jejunum		13	13a	14a		177
ileum		14	13b	14b		178
ileocecal valve		15	14	15		182
plica circularis		35		8		
lacteals (green)		37 & 40				
villi		38 & 39				
simple columnar epithelium						
goblet cells		44				
arteriole (red)		36 & 41				
venule (blue)		36 & 42				
capillary network (purple)		43				
large intestine/ colon			15	18		179 & 183
cecum		16	15d	16		180
appendix		24	15e	17		181
ascending colon		17	15a	18a		184
right colic (hepatic) flexure		18				
transverse colon		19	15b	18b		185
left colic (splenic) flexure		20				
descending colon		21	15c	18c		186
sigmoid colon		22		18d		187
taenia coli						
haustra						

Structure Name	Teeth Plaque	Digestive System Plaque	Digestive System Model (white base)	Digestive System Model (green base)	Pancreas with Duodenum and Spleen	Torso Model
rectum		23	16	19		188
anal canal			17			
anus						
liver		9	12	13		189
falciform ligament						
hepatic ducts		33				194
gall bladder		10	11	10		197
cystic duct		32	11d			198
common bile duct		34	11e	9	3	199
pancreas		12	9	11	A	200
pancreatic duct (duct of Wirsung)				11a	1	201
accessory pancreatic duct (duct of Santorini)					2	
spleen			10	12	B	202
hepatic portal vein			f	13d	5	192
celiac trunk					8	103
hepatic artery			g	13e	9	193
splenic artery					10	
gastric artery					11	

In dental practice the teeth are numbered starting with the right rear upper molar as #1 continuing around to #16 the left rear upper molar. #17 is the lower left molar with #32 the lower right molar. Teeth numbers 1, 16, 17 and 32 are called the wisdom teeth because they erupt around 18 to 21 years of age. Complications often arise because the jaws of many adults are not large enough to accommodate all 32 teeth. Without the wisdom teeth the numbering scheme runs 2-15 and 18-31.

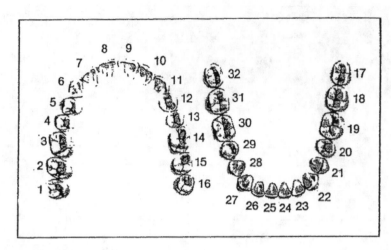

Figure 1. The tooth numbering scheme used in current dental practice.

Cats may be available for your observation. Your instructor may ask you to be able to locate and identify the following structures on the dissected cats.

Parotid salivary gland
Esophagus
Stomach with rugae
Small intestine, duodenum and ileum portions
Large intestine with cecum
Liver
Gall bladder
Pancreas
Spleen (while not a part of the digestive system, this is a good opportunity to observe it)
Mesentery and Greater omentum

II. MICROSCOPIC ANATOMY OF THE DIGESTIVE SYSTEM

Introduction

From the esophagus to the anus the GI tract/alimentary canal wall has four basic layers. The **mucosa** lines the gut and is usually a simple columnar epithelium. It also includes the connective tissue called the **lamina propria** and the thin smooth muscle layer called the **muscularis mucosae**. The **submucosa** is areolar (loose) connective tissue connecting the mucosa to the muscularis. In some regions the density of collagenous and elastic fibers is great and a histologist could consider this as a dense connective tissue. The submucosa is highly vascularized and supplied with nerve endings. The **muscularis (or muscularis externa)**, with some exceptions, consists of a circular inner layer of smooth muscle and an outer layer with longitudinal fibers. The mouth, pharynx and upper half of esophagus have skeletal muscle to facilitate voluntary swallowing. The stomach has three, rather than two, layers of smooth muscle. The smooth muscle is well supplied with branches of the autonomic nervous system to control its motility.

The outer layer of these hollow organs is the **serosa** also called the visceral peritoneum. The serosa is simple squamous epithelium along with its thin layer of underlying connective tissue.

In the mucosa, the nonkeratinized stratified squamous epithelium lining the esophagus changes to a simple columnar epithelium at the cardia of the stomach. Within the stomach, many of the simple columnar cells on the surface produce mucus. Alkaline mucus is secreted to coat and protect the cells from the digestive action of stomach acid and enzymes. These columnar cells dip down into the lamina propria. The lamina propria is very thin in the stomach. When the columnar cells dip down into the lamina propria, they form **gastric pits.** At the base of every gastric pit are **gastric glands**. Within the gastric glands there are four types of cells. The most numerous are the **chief (zymogenic) cells**, which secrete the inactive protein digesting enzyme **pepsinogen. Parietal cells** secrete **hydrochloric acid** that activates pepsinogen to active pepsin. The HCl is also useful in the hydrolysis of collagen fibers found in connective tissue that binds muscle. Parietal cells also secrete the **intrinsic factor** that promotes the absorption of vitamin B_{12}. The **G cells** produce the hormone **gastrin**. The last type of cells in the gastric glands is the **mucous neck cells** that also produce mucus.

In the small intestines the mucosa is permanently folded into structures called **plicae circulares (s. plica circularis)** to increase the surface area inside the intestines for greater absorption. There is a core of submucosa in every plica. To further increase surface area, the epithelium is folded into structures called **villi (s. villus)** on the surface of the plicae. Villi are finger-like protrusions of the intestinal lining into the lumen. The lamina propria fills the core of a villus containing connective tissue, lymphatic nodules and networks of capillaries and lymph vessels. The lamina propria contains nerves and the capillary network into which the products of digestion are absorbed. Villi also contain the network of lymphatic vessels called the **lacteals** that absorb lipids. These vessels are not easily observable under light microscopy. The muscularis mucosae does not enter an individual villus. Imbedded in the lamina propria of the mucosa at the base of the villi are the circles of glandular cells called the **intestinal glands (Crypts of Lieberkühn** or sometimes intestinal crypts). These secrete intestinal digestive enzymes. In the duodenum, pockets of epithelial tissue extend through the muscularis mucosae into the submucosa forming glands called **Brunner's** or **duodenal glands**. These secrete alkaline mucus to help neutralize the pH of the stomach contents (chyme) as it enters the small intestine. The ileum is the last part of the small intestine. Duodenal (Brunner's) glands are absent from the ileum. Here, as well as in the middle segment called the jejunum, the columnar epithelium of the mucosa contains numerous mucus secreting **goblet cells. Lymphatic nodules** also called **Peyer's patches** are scattered through the lamina propria of the mucosa in the small intestine. Lymphatic nodules help protect the body from infection, and these associated with the gut are possibly important for development of the capacity for antibody production.

The large intestine lacks the folds and villi of the small intestine. The lining is rather smooth. The histology resembles that of the ileum sufficiently that we will not spend time with it.

Among the accessory structures of the digestive system are the salivary glands. The salivary glands are composed of groups of cells called **acini (s. acinous)** surrounded by connective tissue. Acini are clusters of epithelial tissue. Some of the acini are collections of mucus secreting cells called **mucous acini**. (mucus = noun; mucous = adjective) Other collections secrete watery secretions that contain the enzyme, salivary amylase. The **sublingual salivary gland** contains mostly mucous acini with few serous acini, the parotid salivary gland has all serous acini, and the submandibular gland will have mostly serous and some mucous acini. The products of the acini are transported to the mouth through **excretory ducts**, which are lined with simple cuboidal epithelium.

Procedure

Salivary Gland

1. Obtain a slide labeled **"Salivary gland, sublingual, Human"**

2. Focus with scanning, low, and then high power.

3. Identify the purplish clusters as gland tissue. The lighter clusters are mucous acini and the darker clusters are serous acini.

4. Look for a small excretory duct.

5. Draw a mucous acinous, a serous acini and an excretory duct in the POST-LAB OBSERVATION section.

Stomach

1. Obtain a slide labeled **"Stomach, body, dog, general structure"**

2. Use the scanning objective to orient to the slide and observe the mucosa, submucosa, muscularis, and serosa layers.

3. Make a sketch of these layers in the POST-LAB OBSERVATION section.

4. Locate the mucosa on scanning power and then focus under low and then high power. Note the layer of simple columnar epithelium that comprises the stomach lining. The ends of the epithelial cells that face the lumen of the stomach are light pink in color and are filled with mucus.

5. These columnar cells dip down into the lamina propria. The lamina propria is very thin in the stomach and you will not be able to see it on your slide.

6. Identify the gastric pits and gastric glands. Identify the numerous, small, darkly staining chief (zymogenic) cells. The larger pink cells with a central nucleus are the parietal cells.

7. Locate the thin layer of smooth muscle called the muscularis mucosae, lying between the lamina propria and the submucosa.

8. Make a sketch of the mucosa in the POST-LAB OBSERVATION section.

Small Intestine – Duodenum

1. Obtain a slide labeled **"Duodenum, Human"**

2. With the scanning objective locate the mucosa, submucosa and muscularis externa and note the plicae circulares (=circular folds). You may also see the outer layer called the serosa or visceral peritoneum adjacent to the muscularis. The boundary between the mucosa and submucosa is a thin layer of smooth muscle tissue called the muscularis mucosae. It is the distinct pink layer below the epithelium following the contours of the plicae circularis.

3. On low power, note the villi on the surface of the folds. Each villus is covered with simple columnar epithelium, which is best seen at high power. The muscularis mucosae does not enter an individual villus.

4. Identify the intestinal glands, Crypts of Lieberkühn and the duodenal (Brunner's) glands.

5. Distinguish the circular and longitudinal layers of smooth muscle in the muscularis externa. Remember the inner smooth muscle layer encircles the intestine while the outer layer runs longitudinally. On this slide you will be viewing the cells of the circular muscle layer in cross section.

6. The serosa may or may not be visible. Under high power you should see individual simple squamous epithelial cells, each with a flattened oval nucleus.

7. Make a sketch of all of the layers of the duodenum in the POST-LAB OBSERVATION section.

Small Intestine – Ileum

1. Obtain the slide labeled **"Ileum, human sec."**

2. With the scanning objective locate the mucosa, submucosa, the circular layer of the muscularis externa, the longitudinal layer of the muscularis externa, the plicae circulares, the simple columnar epithelium, the villi, the intestinal glands, the mucularis mucosae, and possibly the serosa.

3. Find a large lymphatic nodule (Peyer's patch) within the lamina propria of the mucosa.

4. Note the differences between the duodenum and the ileum. Be able to distinguish between the two structures.

5. In the space provided in the POST-LAB OBSERVATIONS section draw a portion of the ileum and label the structures listed.

Digestive System Microscopic Structures

Structure Name – Salivary Gland
mucous acinous
serous acinous
excretory duct

Structure Name – Stomach
mucosa
mucularis mucosae
simple columnar epithelium
gastric pits
gastric glands
chief (zymogenic) cells
parietal cells
submucosa
muscularis externa
serosa

Structure Name – Duodenum
mucosa
lamina propria
muscularis mucosae
simple columnar epithelium
intestinal glands (crypts of Lieberkühn)
plica circularis
submucosa
duodenal gland (Brunner's gland)
lymphatic nodules (Peyer's patches)
circular layer of muscularis externa
longitudinal layer muscularis externa
serosa

Structure Name – Ileum
mucosa
lamina propria
muscularis mucosae
simple columnar epithelium
intestinal glands (crypts of Lieberkühn)
plica circularis
lymphatic nodules (Peyer's patches)
submucosa
circular layer of muscularis externa
longitudinal layer muscularis externa
serosa

III. INTRODUCTION TO DIGESTIVE FUNCTION USING PHYSIOEX 8.0

Introduction

In this exercise you are going to get an introduction to digestive physiology using a computer lab simulation program. In this experiment you are going to explore the effect of a digestive enzyme, amylase, on different nutrients. In addition, the effects of changing conditions, such as pH and temperature will be looked at. This simulation is a preview of one of the experiments that will be completed in the next laboratory exercise.

Procedure

Initial Preparation

6. Proceed as a group to the computer assigned to you.

7. Open PhysioEx 8.0. You do not need to click on site requirements. Just click **Enter**.

8. If your computer prompts you to allow blocked content, always allow blocked content.

9. Choose Exercise 8. Process of Digestion at top of page with the down arrow. Click **Go**.

10. Click on the **Amylase** experiment.

You will notice test tubes on the left side and what represents an incubator on the right side with seven slots for test tubes. Dropper vials in the upper right are filled with various substances.

Experimental Set-up

10. Click on a test tube and drag it to the first slot on the incubator. Repeat this procedure one at a time with the remaining 6 tubes.

11. Set the temperature at 37 degrees C and the timer to 60 minutes.

12. Click on the dropper of the proper vial and drag it to the tube to add reagents to the tubes. Add the reagents marked with an X on the following table.

Reagent	Tube 1	Tube 2	Tube 3	Tube 4	Tube 5	Tube 6	Tube 7
Starch	X	X	X	X	X		
Cellulose						X	X
pH 7 buffer	X	X	X		X	X	X
pH 2 buffer				X			
Amylase	X	X	X	X		X	
Peptidase					X		
Bacteria							X

Running the Experiment

1. Click on the number **below** tube #2. It will lower into the incubator. Click on **Boil** on the right side of the incubator. This will boil this sample.

2. Click on the number **below** tube #3. It will lower into the incubator. Click on **Freeze**. This will freeze the sample.

3. Now, click on **Incubate**. All the tubes will drop into the incubator and simulate incubating for 60 minutes. (It will not really take 60 minutes; it will only take 60 seconds!) When the elapsed time reaches 60 the tubes will automatically rise from the incubator and a door will open in a cabinet in the upper left.

4. Click on the first **tube** (not the number). You can now drag it (as a small version) to the cabinet and place it over the #1 tube within the cabinet. You will observe a "sample" pouring into the corresponding tube in the cabinet. Repeat this with the remaining 6 tubes in turn.

5. When all samples are in the cabinet, click on the **IKI dropper**, drag and release it over tube #1. It will automatically dispense IKI to this and all the other tubes as well. If you see the tube turn dark, this is a positive test for starch (or cellulose). Starch and cellulose are both chains of glucose units.

6. Observe which tubes turned dark and which did not and record which tubes were positive for starch or cellulose in the POST-LAB OBSERVATION section.

7. Now, click on the dropper of **Benedict's solution** and drag it over the tube #1 **in the incubator**. Repeat for each tube within the incubator.

   Benedict's solution is a chemical test that is used to detect the presence of reducing sugars, such as maltose and glucose. The sample tubes with Benedict's reagent must be heated in order for the test to work. A positive test with Benedict's reagent is shown by a color change from clear blue to green to brick-red depending upon the amount of reducing sugars present.

8. When all the tubes have Benedict's, click on **Boil**. A Benedict's test requires a boiling water bath although the sample itself does not boil. After boiling, the tubes will rise from the incubator.

9. Observe the color each tube turned and record their colors in the POST-LAB OBSERVATION section.

10. Click on **Record Data**.

11. Click **Tools → Print Data** at the top of the page to print your data.

12. Observe the data and answer the questions in the POST-LAB OBSERVATION section.

PRE-LAB QUESTIONS

Name _____

Answer these questions by reading the lab manual prior to coming to lab!

A. Name the four different types of teeth normally found in an adult's jaw.

_____

_____

_____

_____

B. What are some ways that the gut of carnivores differs from our own?

C. What two ducts unite to form the common bile duct?

_____ and_____

D. What are the four layers of the GI tract/alimentary canal?

_____

_____

_____

_____

E. How long is the adult GI tract/alimentary canal? _____

F. What structures are absent from the ileum but present in the duodenum?

G. What is secreted by the chief (zymogenic) cells? _____

H. What substances are secreted by the parietal cells? _____

From the History:

I. The pancreatic duct was formerly known by the eponym of _____.

J. What happened to the person who first described the duct?

K. Gross Anatomy of the Digestive System

    1. Label these major parts of the GI tract.

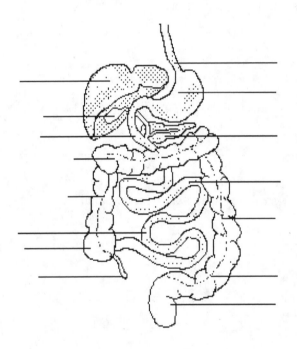

2. Label the regions of the stomach

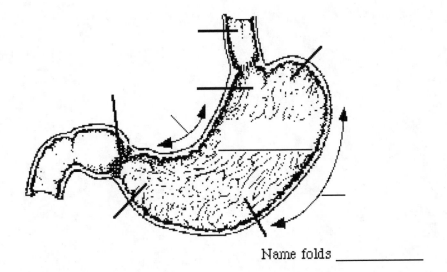

Name folds _____

3. Label structures of the large intestine.

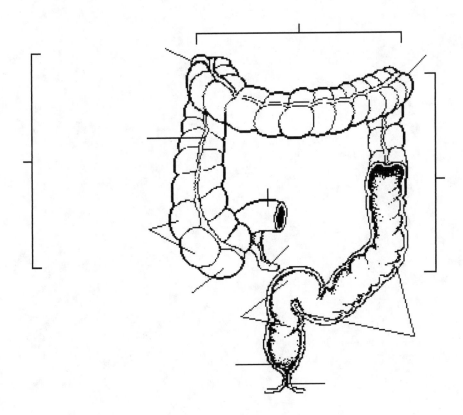

III. INTRODUCTION TO DIGESTIVE FUNCTION USING PHYSIOEX 8.0

A. Which tubes are positive for starch or cellulose? _____

B. List the color of the tubes after a Benedict's test

	Tube 1	Tube 2	Tube 3	Tube 4	Tube 5	Tube 6	Tube 7
Color							

A reddish-brown color indicates a high amount of maltose, a disaccharide composed of two glucose units or glucose. A green color indicates a slight amount. A negative test for maltose or glucose is blue.

C. Was starch digested to maltose in tube #1 by the amylase? _____(Y/N)

    a. Explain why amylase digested or did not digest starch to maltose or glucose this tube.

D. Was starch digested to maltose in tube #2? _____ (Y/N)

    a. Explain why amylase digested or did not digest starch to maltose or glucose this tube. (Remember, you boiled the enzyme so explain the significance of this.)

E. Was starch digested to maltose in tube #3? _____(Y/N)

    a. Explain why amylase digested or did not digest starch to maltose or glucose this tube. (Remember that we froze this tube, so explain the significance of that.)

F. Was starch completely digested to maltose in tube #4?_____ (Y/N)
    Partly?_____ (Y/N) (hint: color of Benedict's)

    a. Explain why amylase digested or did not digest starch to maltose or glucose this tube. (Remember, we changed the pH of the buffer.)

G. Was starch digested to maltose in tube #5? _____ (Y/N)

    a. Explain why peptidase digested or did not digest starch to maltose or glucose this tube.

H. Was cellulose digested to maltose in tube #6 by the amylase? _____ (Y/N)

    a. Explain why amylase digested or did not digest cellulose to maltose or glucose this tube. (This could be tricky as both starch and cellulose are chains of glucose units but they are bonded to each other in a different way.)

I. Was cellulose digested to maltose in tube #7 by the bacteria? _____ (Y/N)

    a. Explain why bacteria digested or did not digest cellulose to maltose or glucose this tube.

    b. How do you think herbivores such as cows, horses and termites manage to digest cellulose?

J. Clinical thinking: From your data, which do you think would be worse for enzyme action? A high prolonged fever or hypothermia? Explain your answer.

DIGESTION AND ABSORPTION

HISTORY

Digestive physiology has been studied by many scientists. Some very interesting findings, however, were made by an American, William Beaumont, who had never been to medical school, but was apprenticed to a doctor and became a surgeon in the US Army. In 1822 he attended to a young Canadian who had received a gunshot wound in the abdomen. The man survived the surgery with a permanent fistula in his stomach. Beaumont became fascinated with his patient's unique defect and took advantage of it to study the process of digestion. He asked the man to swallow different foods, tying pieces of silk thread to them so that they could be pulled up again for examination. He also collected stomach contents via a tube passed into the fistula. In 1833, after many years' work, Beaumont published a book called *Observations on the Gastric Juice and the Physiology of Digestion*. His fifty-one conclusions are still valid today.

OBJECTIVES

1. To use some common chemical tests for food substances and their hydrolysis products.
2. To observe the action of certain digestive tract secretions on foods.

I. STARCH DIGESTION

Introduction

Complex animals use their digestive system to both obtain and process food. In order for food to be absorbed into the blood and lymph vessels it must be broken down into molecules small enough to pass through cell membranes. Food is digested mechanically by chewing and the churning action of the stomach. Chemical digestion by hydrolytic enzymes in the mouth, stomach and small intestine produces small molecules that are absorbed and then distributed throughout the body by the circulatory system. **Hydrolysis** involves the splitting of large molecules into smaller ones by the addition of water molecules.

Starch, also known as amylose, is a polysaccharide of glucose. The salivary glands produce the enzyme **amylase**, which hydrolyzes the starch molecules into **maltose**. Since maltose is a disaccharide, it is still too large to readily diffuse into the blood. When the food is swallowed amylase is inactivated by the acidic conditions in the stomach. In the small intestine amylase and maltase, produced by the intestinal wall and pancreas, are added to the partially digested food. These enzymes will complete the hydrolysis of amylose and maltose to **glucose**. Glucose molecules are small enough to move through the intestinal wall and into the circulatory system.

Cellulose, another polysaccharide of glucose, is a common component of the plant cell wall and in turn of our diet. We lack the enzyme cellulase, therefore cannot digest cellulose. Cellulose is hydroscopic, so water clings to it as do many other potentially harmful chemicals found in our food. Whole grains, fruits and vegetables contain cellulose, thus providing crucial fiber in our diet.

Procedures

THINK about what you are doing in this procedure. It follows a simple but classic form for an experimental design. Add components to your tubes according to the table.

Reagent	Tube A	Tube B	Tube C	Tube D	Tube E
Starch	1/8 tsp	1/8 tsp		1/8 tsp	1/8 tsp
Water	10ml	10 ml	8ml	8ml	8ml
Saliva			2ml	2ml	2ml
IKI	5 drops				5 drops
Benedict's solution		10 drops	10 drops	10 drops	

1. Wash 5 test tubes and label them A, B, C, D, and E.

2. Add appropriate amount of water to each tube.

3. Place 1/8 tsp of starch in test tubes A and B. Place a piece of Parafilm and your thumb over the mouth of the tube and shake the tube to thoroughly mix the starch with the water.

4. Place 5 drops of iodine (IKI) in tube A and shake it. A black, purple or dark blue color indicates the presence of starch. Save this tube and the others for comparison at the end of all tests. If the solution does not turn purple or black, the IKI solution has deteriorated. If this is the case, give the bottle of bad iodine to the instructor and add 5 drops of iodine from another bottle to your tube A.

5. Add 10 drops of Benedicts' solution to tube B, shake it up, remove the Parafilm and place in the heat block. Shortly before it begins to boil, remove the tube from the heat using a test tube holder and place in the test tube rack to cool.

6. Add 2ml of water to a clean test tube and mark the fluid level on the side of the tube. Empty the test tube.

7. Collect 2 ml of saliva by spitting into the marked test tube and then pour the saliva into test tube C. Rinse your mouth with water before starting, if you have just had food or a sugar containing drink or gum in your mouth. You may chew a piece of sugarless gum, to encourage salivation. **The person spitting should be the only person to handle tubes C, D and E.**

8. Add 10 drops of Benedicts' solution to tube C and shake it up after covering the tube with Parafilm. The shaking corresponds to the gut movement called **peristalsis**. Remove the Parafilm and place tube C in the heat block to heat the tube. After the sample has been in the heat block for a time, check for the presence of sugar in saliva.

9. Collect another 2 ml of saliva in the marked test tube and add to tube D. Also add 1/8 tsp of starch. Cover the tube with Parafilm and shake tube. Let stand for at least 2 minutes.

10. Repeat step 9 for tube E.

11. Add 10 drops of Benedicts' solution to tube D and shake to mix. Remove Parafilm and heat, to test for sugar as in steps 5 and 7.

12. Add 5 drops of iodine to test tube E cover with Parafilm and shake to test for the presence of starch.

13. Record all results in the POST-LAB OBSERVATIONS section and answer the questions. The following information will help you answer the questions.

Sugars, such as maltose and glucose, reduce Benedicts' solution producing a precipitate. The amount of reducing sugar present can be estimated as follows:

Negative - Solution is clear sky blue to green after boiling. (-)

Trace - no precipitate during boiling but when cooled the solution appears turbid-green and a slight yellow to orange precipitate forms. (+)

Moderate amount - yellow or yellow-green precipitate forms after the solution has boiled 15 seconds. (++)

Large amount - orange to red precipitate forms upon boiling indicating almost immediate reduction. (+++)

14. Be prepared to show all of the test tubes to the instructor and to discuss your observations.

15. Place the tubes in the test tube racks by the sink without emptying after the instructor has gone over the results.

II. DIGESTION and ABSORPTION OF FATS

Introduction

Triglycerides are high-energy content molecules stored by animals and also to some extent by plants. A triglyceride molecule consists of **glycerol** combined with three **fatty acids**. A fatty acid consists of a long hydrocarbon chain with a -COOH group at one end. This group becomes acidic if free, but is not acidic when combined with the glycerol. In combination, it is termed a "neutral fat". If the fatty acids in the fat are saturated with hydrogen, it is a **saturated fat** and will be a solid at room temperature. Most animal fats (lard) are saturated fats. Some plants have saturated fats such as cocoa butter, palm and coconut oil. Unsaturated triglycerides have one or more double covalent bonds within the fatty acid chain. They are liquid at room temperature, so we call them **oils.** Plant triglycerides and triglycerides found in fish are oils that often have more than one double covalent bond so are termed **polyunsaturated.**

Our diets frequently include a large portion of fats and oils. Fats and oils are relatively non-polar molecules and thus dissolve poorly in water. Even though fats and oils are significant components of all cell membranes, they do not pass readily through the epithelium. They must be hydrolyzed into smaller molecules in order to be absorbed. In order for these triglycerides to be digested efficiently they must be **emulsified** into tiny colloidal droplets, which expose considerably greater surface area to the action of digestive enzymes. **Bile** is the substance in the intestine that acts as an emulsifying agent breaking up the large fat globules into colloidal size droplets, which will mix with water. Bile thus increases both surface area and solubility. A small "fat blob" covered with bile is called a **micelle.**

Bile is a solution of water, cholesterol, fatty acids, salts, and pigments formed by the liver from the breakdown products of hemoglobin. If the liver is not functioning properly the bile pigments may not be removed from the blood. Excess amounts of bilirubin, the chief bile pigment, in blood cause the eyes and skin to become yellow, a condition called jaundice. Bile not only emulsifies fats but also helps neutralize the acidic chyme and facilitates the absorption of products of fat digestion.

Lipase is an enzyme produced by the pancreas that hydrolyzes fats into its components: **glycerol** and **fatty acids**. Once inside the intestinal cells, these are now re-synthesized into fat, combined with other lipids and covered with protein. These "packages" are now called "**chylomicrons**". These "fat packages" are absorbed into the **lacteals** or lymph vessels rather than the capillaries, as the pores in the walls of the lacteals are larger than those of the blood capillaries. After a meal, the lacteals are filled with this white fatty substance. This milk-like appearance led to the term "lacteal" or milk channel.

Procedures

The Action of Bile on Fats

Reagent	Tube F	Tube G
Corn oil	2 ml	2ml
Water	10 ml	10 ml
Sudan Red	6 drops	6 drops
Dilute Dawn "bile"		1 drop

1. Wash two test tubes and label them A and B.

2. Place 2 ml of corn oil (a polyunsaturated fat) in test tube F. Add 10 ml of distilled water and 6 drops of Sudan Red. Make sure you shake the Sudan Red well before use. Cover the tube with Parafilm and your thumb and shake. Sudan Red "clings" to fat droplets and should be a pink color. If it is not pink, add more Sudan Red. Note the distinct layer of oil floating on the water in large "lava lamp" blobs.

3. Place 2 ml of corn oil in test tube G. Add 10 ml of distilled water, 6 drops of Sudan Red and **one** drop of liquid detergent. The detergent has the same action on the oil droplets as bile does, and it is much more convenient to use. Place Parafilm and your thumb over the mouth of this test tube and shake vigorously. Set the tubes in your test tube rack.

4. Compare the size of the droplets in tubes F and G. Note the color of the water in tube G.

5. Record all results in the POST-LAB OBSERVATIONS section and answer the questions.

The Action of Lipase on Fats

Reagent	Tube H	Tube I	Tube J	Tube K
Litmus Milk	4ml	4ml	4ml	4ml
Pancreatin = lipase		5ml		5ml
Water	5ml		5ml	
Dilute Dawn "bile"			1 drop	1 drop

1. Label 4 clean test tubes with your initials and H, I, J or K.

2. Place 4 ml of litmus milk (containing saturated fat) in each tube. A 1% litmus solution was added to half and half as a pH indicator, producing a light blue-purple color. Remember: litmus has a pink color in acid solution while in alkaline solution it is blue.

3. Tube H is the control. Add 5 ml of water to control for the addition of enzyme.

4. To the litmus milk of tube I, add 5 ml of 2% pancreatin solution, which contains the enzyme lipase.

5. To the litmus milk of tube J, add one drop of detergent (= bile) and 5 ml of water.

6. To the litmus milk of tube K, add one drop of detergent and 5 ml of the lipase solution.

7. Cover all tubes with Parafilm and shake.

8. Place all tubes in the 37°C temperature controlled water bath for 15 minutes.

9. Examine the tubes for color changes after incubating 15 min.

10. Record all results in the POST-LAB OBSERVATIONS section and answer the questions.

11. Place the tubes in the test tube racks by the sink without emptying after the instructor has gone over the results.

III. ABSORPTION THROUGH THE INTESTINAL WALL

Introduction

Most of the end products of digestion move through the columnar epithelial cells lining the intestine by osmosis and diffusion. The membranes of the intestinal lining are **selectively permeable** allowing only certain molecules to pass through. Generally, discrimination is based on the size of the molecule and its charge. Small, non-polar molecules are absorbed most readily. The separation of substances in a solution by means of their unequal diffusion through a selectively permeable membrane is termed **dialysis**. Material not absorbed will be excreted as feces.

Procedures

Immersed in a beaker of distilled water is a bag containing a solution of starch, glucose, and sodium chloride. The water in the graduated cylinder represents the **blood** while the bag is of permeability similar to the **small intestine.** You now need to sample the surrounding "blood" and determine what substances have been absorbed through the "small intestinal wall".

Reagent	Tube L	Tube M	Tube N	Starch +	Starch -
Sample from large graduated cylinder	5ml	5ml	5ml		
Benedict's solution	10 drops				
IKI		5 drops		5 drops	5 drops
AgNO$_3$			2 drops		
Starch				1/8 tsp	
Water				5ml	5ml

1. Label 3 clean test tubes L, M and N.

2. Place 5 ml of fluid from the large graduated cylinder into each of the test tubes.

3. Add 10 drops of Benedict's solution to tube L. Cover tube with Parafilm and shake. Remove the Parafilm. Heat the solution in a heat block. See page 9-3 for interpretation of results.

4. Test for the presence of starch in tube M by adding 5 drops of iodine (IKI). Cover tube with Parafilm and shake.

5. Add a drop or two of silver nitrate to tube N. Cover tube with Parafilm and shake.

$$Ag\,NO_3 + Na\,Cl \rightarrow Ag\,Cl + Na\,NO_3$$

The appearance of a white precipitate or cloudiness indicates the presence of silver chloride and is thus a positive test for the presence of Cl^- in the solution.

6. You will have to also set up a positive and a negative control for the starch test. To do this, mark one tube + and add 1/8 tsp of starch, 5 ml of water and 5 drops of iodine (IKI). Mark the other tube – and add 5 ml of water and 5 drops of iodine (IKI). Cover both tubes with Parafilm and shake. A black precipitate indicates the presence of starch.

7. Answer questions in the POST-LAB OBSERVATIONS section. Think about which type of substances are absorbed and why.

8. Place the tubes in the test tube racks by the sink without emptying after the instructor has gone over the results.

PRE-LAB QUESTIONS   **Name**_____

A. Define:

1. hydrolysis

2. selectively permeable

3. starch

4. fatty acid

5. saturated fat

6. polyunsaturated

7. lipase

8. lacteals

9. From the History: How did Beaumont study digestive enzymes?

POST-LAB OBSERVATIONS

I. STARCH DIGESTION

A. Fill in table:

Tube	Substance to Test	Test Reagent Added (iodine or Benedict's)	Result of Test (-/+ for starch or -/+ for maltose)
A	starch		
B	starch		
C	saliva		
D	starch & saliva		
E	starch & saliva		

B. The black color of test tube A indicated that _____ was present.

C. Was maltose present in the undigested starch in tube B? _____ (Y/N)

    1. How do you know?

D. Was maltose or glucose present in your saliva in tube C? _____ (Y/N)

    1. How do you know?

E. Was the Benedict's test for maltose or glucose in tube D positive? _____ (Y/N)

F. Compare tubes B and D. Which has the most maltose and glucose? _____

G. Was any of the starch hydrolyzed (broken down) by the saliva? _____ (Y/N)

    1. How do you know?

H. Was all of the starch hydrolyzed? _____

    1. How do you know? (Hint: consider tube E results.)

I. Name the substance responsible for the hydrolysis of starch in your mouth and where it is produced.

J. What advantages can you describe for chewing one's food thoroughly?

II. DIGESTION AND ABSORPTION OF FATS

The Action of Bile on Fats

A. What difference do you observe in the size of the droplets in the two test tubes?

B. Name the process that produced the effect when detergent is added to the fat?

C. What action of the intestine corresponds with the shaking of the test tubes?

D. How does the emulsification of fat aid in its digestion?

The Action of Lipase on Fats

A. Fill in the table:

Tube	Reagents added to tube	Color after 15 minutes
H		
I		
J		
K		

B. What substance(s) cause hydrolysis of fat? _____

C. List the products of fat hydrolysis? _____

D. Which of the product(s) of fat hydrolysis resulted in the color change observed in tube I?

_____

E. Compare tubes I and K. Is more litmus milk hydrolyzed when 'bile' is present? _____(Y/N)

F. Does bile (i.e. the detergent) cause fat hydrolysis? _____

1. How do you know?

G. Does a significant amount of fat digestion occur by body temperature alone? _____(Y/N)
    (hint: consider tube H)

H. Are the products of the action of lipase on fat small enough molecules to be absorbed?
    _____(Y/N)

I. Are the oil droplets produced by the action of bile small enough to be absorbed?
    _____(Y/N)

III. ABSORPTION THROUGH THE INTESTINAL WALL

A. Was glucose present in tube L? _____(Y/N)

B. Was starch present in tube M? _____(Y/N)

C. Was salt present in tube N? _____(Y/N)

D. Which substances were absorbed through the "intestinal wall"? _____

    1. Why?

E. Was starch absorbed through the "intestinal wall"? _____(Y/N)

    1. How do you know?

ENDOCRINE SYSTEM ANATOMY & HISTOLOGY

HISTORY

Aristotle believed that the function of the entire brain was to secrete pituita or mucous which it discharged through the nose to cool the body. The pituitary gland itself was not observed until 1524. Nineteen years later, it was referred to in Vesalius' *De Fabrica* as the "glandula pituitam" or phlegm gland. It still retains this name today even though its real functions are known.

A medical student, Paul Langerhans observed the islets that bear his name, but did not determine their function. Claude Bernard did extensive studies of the pancreas, but it was two scientists, von Mering and Minkowski who proved the connection between diabetes mellitus and the pancreas with their work on dogs. In the 1920s a Romanian physiologist Nicolas Paulescu, extracted a hormone from the pancreas he called pancreine and proved that it relieved diabetes in dogs whose pancreas had been removed. He published in a French journal in 1921. This was known to Frederick Banting and Charles Best, Canadian physiologists, who later published virtually the same work. They called their extract insulin and with the help of Eli Lilly company produced insulin on a commercial scale. The 1933 Nobel Prize was not rewarded to Paulescu nor to Best, but to Banting and J.R. McLeod who directed the Toronto laboratories. Paulescu later died, some say, of a broken heart.

OBJECTIVES

1. To identify the major endocrine organs and their location in the body.
2. To examine a slide of the pancreas and identify both the exocrine and the endocrine histology

I. GROSS ANATOMY OF THE ENDOCRINE SYSTEM

Introduction

Exocrine glands, such as sweat and salivary glands, secrete their products through a duct or tube. **Endocrine glands,** on the other hand, secrete their products directly into the bloodstream. The word endocrine means to "secrete within". The products that endocrine glands secrete are **hormones**. Hormones are often defined as chemical messengers that travel in the blood and act at a site distant from their release. Hormones act on **target** cells that possess specific three-dimensional **receptors** for the particular hormone. Hormones are considered to be a very basic form of cell-to-cell communication as hormones and receptors have been found in all plants and animals.

Many different hormone-secreting glands make up the endocrine system. These glands include the pituitary gland, the thyroid gland, the parathyroid gland, the adrenal gland, and the pineal gland. The primary function of these glands is as endocrine glands. There are also organs that produce hormones as a secondary function, such as the hypothalamus, thymus, pancreas, ovaries, testes, kidneys, stomach, liver, small intestine, skin, heart, placenta, and adipose tissue.

The **hypothalamus** is the major integrating link between the nervous and endocrine systems. The hypothalamus controls the release of hormones from the pituitary gland with releasing and inhibiting hormones. It is also the site of production of **oxytocin** and **anti-diuretic hormone** which are released from the posterior pituitary.

The **pituitary gland**, located just inferior to the brain, is referred to as the "master" gland as it regulates virtually all aspects of growth, development, metabolism, and homeostasis. The pituitary is divided into the anterior and posterior pituitary gland. The anterior pituitary gland produces the following hormones: **human growth hormone (hGH), thyroid-stimulating hormone (TSH), follicle-stimulating hormone (FSH), luteinizing hormone (LH), prolactin (PRL), adrenocorticotrophic hormone (ACTH), and melanocyte-stimulating hormone (MSH)**.

The **thyroid gland** is located just below the larynx and has right and left lateral lobes. Thyroid follicles secrete the thyroid hormones, **thyroxine (T_4)** and **triiodothyronine (T_3)**, and cells between the follicles, parafollicular cells, secrete **calcitonin (CT)**. The thyroid hormones help regulate basal metabolic rate and stimulate protein synthesis. Calcitonin helps lower blood calcium levels by promoting bone synthesis.

The four **parathyroid glands** are embedded on the posterior surfaces of the lateral lobes of the thyroid gland. **Parathyroid hormone (PTH)** is the principal hormone of the parathyroid gland. Parathyroid hormone (PTH) regulates the homeostasis of calcium and phosphate. It increases blood calcium levels by increasing the number and activity of osteoclasts and promoting the reabsorption of calcium by the distal convoluted tubules within the kidneys.

The **adrenal glands** are located superior to the kidneys and have an outer layer, the **adrenal cortex** and an inner core, the **adrenal medulla**. The cortex is further divided into three zones; the **zona glomerulosa** (outer zone), the **zona fasciculata** (middle zone), and the **zona reticularis** (inner zone). The zona glomerulosa secretes mineralocorticoids, mainly **aldosterone**, which helps regulate water and sodium homeostasis. Glucocorticoids, such as **cortisol**, are secreted from the zona fasciculata. Cortisol is the main hormone that provides resistance to stress by making nutrients available for ATP production. The zona reticularis produces androgens. The adrenal medulla enhances the function of the sympathetic autonomic nervous system by secreting **epinephrine** and **norepinephrine** into the bloodstream.

The **pancreas** is an organ that has collections of specialized cells, the **pancreatic islets (islets of Langerhans)** that secrete hormones which help regulate metabolism. The islets contain four types of cells: the **alpha cells**, which produce **glucagon**; the **beta cells**, which produce **insulin**; the **delta cells**, which produce **somatostatin**; and **F cells**, which produce **pancreatic polypeptide**. Insulin will lower blood glucose levels, while glucagon will raise them.

The **ovaries** and **testes** primary function is to produce the reproductive cells, eggs and sperm. In addition the ovaries produce the hormones **estrogen, progesterone, relaxin** and **inhibin**, which help regulate the reproductive cycle, maintain pregnancy and prepare the mammary glands for lactation. The testes produce **testosterone** and inhibin, which regulate sperm production and secondary sexual characteristics.

Procedures

1. Locate the structures listed below on the Hubbard Endocrine System plaque.

Structure Name	Endocrine Plaque
pituitary gland (hypophysis)	1
anterior pituitary (adenohypophysis)	2
posterior pituitary (neurohypophysis)	3
infundibulum	4
thyroid gland	5
parathyroid gland	8
adrenal gland (suprarenal gland)	9
adrenal cortex	11
adrenal medulla	12
pancreatic islets (islets of Langerhans)	13
testis	16
ovary	20
corpus luteum	24
pancreas	31

2. Other models of endocrine glands are available for your study. Please learn the locations of the endocrine glands shown on all the models. The structure and location of selected endocrine glands may be demonstrated by your instructor on the cat or the cadaver.

II. MICROSCOPIC ANATOMY OF THE ENDOCRINE SYSTEM

Introduction

In this section we are going to concentrate our interest on one endocrine organ, the pancreas. The pancreas is a compound tubuloacinar gland. The gland is divided into numerous **lobules** by **septa** of connective tissue. The lobules are composed of numerous **pancreatic acini**. The sublingual salivary gland slide you studied previously also contains acini. Both the salivary glands and this digestive portion of the pancreas are exocrine glands. The pancreatic acini produce various digestive enzymes which will be released into the gland's duct work and eventually into the main pancreatic duct which drains into the duodenum. Acinar cells easily comprise at least 99% of the pancreatic cells.

Our interest is really in the endocrine portion of the gland, the **pancreatic islets (islet of Langerhans)**. The islets are clusters of cells that lie between the acini. Four distinct types of endocrine cells form the islets, but they cannot be distinguished on our slides. Special stains are required to react with their unique enzymes and products. All the islet cells will look alike on your slide. **Alpha cells** secrete the hormone **glucagon**. **Beta cells** secrete **insulin**. **Delta cells** produce **somatostatin**, while **F cells** produce **pancreatic polypeptide**. These products are released into the interstitial space and then diffuse into the blood stream for distribution throughout the body.

Elevated blood sugar stimulates the beta cells to release insulin. Insulin facilitates the movement of glucose out of the blood into tissue cells, particularly those in liver. Once in the cells, the glucose may be converted into glycogen or lipids for storage, with these reactions also stimulated by insulin. When blood glucose levels decline below normal, such as with vigorous exercise, the alpha cells are stimulated to release glucagon. Glucagon accelerates the break down of glycogen to glucose to keep blood glucose levels constant. Somatostatin inhibits the secretion of both insulin and glucagon. Pancreatic polypeptide inhibits secretion of somatostatin, gall bladder contraction and secretion of pancreatic digestive enzymes.

Procedures

1. Obtain a slide of the **"Pancreas"**.

2. With the scanning objective observe the general structure of the gland. Identify the lobules and septa, which here appear as clear slits among the purple masses. Within the septa you will recognize blood vessels.

3. Switch to 10X and examine the lobules. Notice the clusters of purple cells, the **pancreatic acini**. Within some lobules are lighter staining masses of cells, the **pancreatic islets (islets of Langerhans)**. The islets lie between the acini.

4. Turn to 40X for study of the exocrine portion of the pancreas, the numerous acini. The acinar cells are purplish at the base of the cell and orangish pink at the apex.

5. Focus on one of the pale staining cell clusters within a lobule, a pancreatic islet. Smaller blood vessels are common within the lobules and they also stain lighter, so do not confuse the two. Blood vessels will have a lumen, which the islets lack. There may or may not be a little space separating the acini and the islets.

6. Draw and label a section of the pancreas in the POST-LAB OBSERVATIONS section.

7. Clean your microscope, lock the scanning objective in place, wind the cord loosely around one eyepiece, put on its dust cover, and return the microscope to the proper location is the microscope cabinet.

Endocrine System Microscopic Structures

Structure Name
lobules
septa
pancreatic acini
pancreatic islets (islets of Langerhans)

REPRODUCTIVE SYSTEM ANATOMY & HISTOLOGY

HISTORY

The reproductive structures of both male and female were described by Aristotle and depicted by Leonardo da Vinci. In 1677 Anton van Leeuwenhoek accurately described the structure of sperm. Although the bulbourethral glands of the male are often still called Cowper's glands, it seems that William Cowper, a London surgeon, who was known for "borrowing" the work of others, took ownership of the discovery in 1702 fifteen years after they were described by the French surgeon Jean Mery. Female anatomy was not as well studied as female cadavers were scarce and also the female body could not be represented unclothed even in the interest of science until the Renaissance. One of the first structures to be described was the uterine tube in 1561 by the Italian anatomist, Gabriele Fallopius. His eponym is so closely associated with the structure that the term fallopian tube is often used without the capital letter. In 1641, a Dutch physician Regnier de Graaf identified the mature ovarian follicle that often bears his name. The suspensory ligaments of the breast are often still referred to as Cooper's ligaments after the English surgeon Astley Cooper who described them in 1845.

OBJECTIVES

1. To identify on models the male and female reproductive organs as well as the menstrual cycle
2. To study the histology of some of the reproductive structures

I. GROSS ANATOMY OF THE REPRODUCTIVE SYSTEM

Introduction

Reproduction is the process of producing offspring by sexual or asexual means in order to propagate the species. In some organisms, new individuals are produced asexually by **mitosis**, which is a type of cell division that results in identical copies of cells. The resulting offspring are all genetically identical to the parent. This gives the population a disadvantage should environmental conditions change. All organisms, even those that can reproduce asexually, use sexual reproduction to give genetic variety to their offspring.

In sexual reproduction, each parent forms sex cells or **gametes** through the cell division process known as **meiosis.** The gametes that result from meiosis have one of each member of a pair of chromosomes of the parent; that is half of the original diploid or 2n number. This is called the **haploid** or n number of chromosomes. When the gametes from the two parents combine, the result is a diploid cell with a new, unique genetic combination. This cell then goes on to divide by mitosis into a new individual. Both plants and animals go through the process of forming gametes and thus possess either **ovaries** or **testes (s. testis)** or their plant analogs. These sex organs produce the gametes and often produce reproductive hormones as well. Many of the other reproductive structures you will study such as the **penis, vagina** and associated structures are only found in animals that must accomplish internal fertilization, which is the combination of gametes within the body of the female parent. **Mammary glands** are unique to mammals.

Female Reproductive System

Ovaries are the primary sex organ of the female reproductive system. They are the site of **egg (ovum or oocyte)** maturation and the site of female hormone (estrogen and progesterone) production. Ovaries are solid, ovoid structures located within the lateral pelvic cavity. They are maintained in position by a series of ligaments. The **broad ligament** suspends the uterus from the side wall of the pelvis; the **mesovarium** attaches the ovaries to the broad ligament; the **ovarian ligament** anchors the ovary to the uterus; the **suspensory ligament** covers the blood vessels to the ovaries; and the **round ligament** attaches the ovaries to the inguinal canal.

The female reproductive system also includes some internal accessory organs. The **uterine tubes (oviducts, Fallopian tubes)** are suspended by the broad ligament and lead to the uterus. The **infundibulum** of the uterine tube is the funnel shaped portion near each ovary. Each uterine tube has **fimbriae**, finger-like projections at the end of the tube near each ovary. The uterine tubes are lined with a ciliated epithelial tissue. The cilia beat in unison, drawing the egg cell into the uterine tube. The **uterus** is the site of fetal development. Anatomically the uterus can be divided into the following regions. The **fundus** is the dome shaped portion superior to the uterine tubes; the **body** is the central portion of the uterus; the **isthmus** (neck) is the constricted portion of the uterus between the body and cervix; and the **cervix** is the inferior portion that opens to the vagina. The **vagina** is a fibromuscular tube that extends from the uterus to the outside.

The female also has a collection of external reproductive organs, called the vulva (pudendum). The **labia majora (s. labium major)** enclose and protect the other external reproductive organs. The **labia minora (s. labium minus)** are flattened, longitudinal folds between the labia majora that form a hood around the clitoris. The **clitoris** is a mass of erectile tissue at the anterior end of the vulva between the labia minora; it corresponds to the male penis. The **vestibule** is the space enclosed by the labia minora into which the vagina opens posteriorly.

The pair of mammary glands form over the pectoralis major muscles in humans rather than the abdominal region as in most other mammals. About 1% of the population has one additional nipple, or perhaps breast, lying superior and lateral, or inferior and medial to the normal nipple. The **mammary glands** are modified sweat glands. **Suspensory ligaments** (Cooper's ligaments) run through the gland attaching the inner layers of the skin to the pectoralis muscle. The varying size of human mammary glands is primarily due to varying amounts of adipose tissue rather than the size of the lactiferous (milk producing) apparatus. The mammary glands are comprised of 20 or so lobes. Each lobe has several smaller compartments or lobules containing clusters of alveoli where the milk is produced. They drain via **mammary ducts** toward the nipple. Near the end each mammary duct will expand into a **lactiferous sinus**. **Lactiferous ducts** lead from the sinus to the surface of the nipple. Lactation is the processes of secretion and ejection of milk from the mammary glands.

In female mammals, there is a very complex hormonal cycle (known in humans as the **menstrual cycle**) that must coordinate activities in the ovary with the preparation of the uterus for implantation of the fertilized egg. The hypothalamus of the brain has a cyclic release of the hormone GNRH. This, in turn controls the anterior pituitary's cycles in the production of the hormones FSH and LH which control the changes in the ovary. The ovaries then vary their production of the hormones estrogen and progesterone, which modulate the cyclic changes in the uterus. The phase of the cycle that precedes ovulation is called the **preovulatory, proliferative** or **follicular phase**. The phase following ovulation is called the **post-ovulatory, secretory, progravid** or **luteal phase**. The phase during which cells and blood are lost is the **menstrual phase**. If the female becomes pregnant menstruation does not occur.

Male Reproductive System

Testes (s. testis) are the primary sex organ of the male reproductive system. They are the site of **sperm (spermatozoa)** and testosterone production. The testes (testicles) are ovoid structures suspended by the spermatic cord in the scrotum. The **scrotum** is a pouch of skin and smooth muscle (dartos muscle) that houses the testes. The scrotum helps regulate the temperature of the testes. Sperm survival requires three degrees lower temperature than core body temperature. The **penis** is the most prominent external male reproductive organ. The penis contains the urethra and is used to deliver the sperm to the female reproductive system. Anatomically, the penis has three regions. The **root** is a combination of the **bulb** and **crura** (s. crus). The **body** is the center section. It contains three erectile tissue masses, the paired **corpora cavernosa penis** (1 & 2) and the unpaired **corpus spongiosum penis** (3). The third region is the distal **glans penis**, which is covered by the **prepuce** or **foreskin**. The foreskin can be removed shortly after the time of birth by circumcision.

The male duct system is a system of tubes designed to transport sperm from the testes to the penis. The **epididymis** is a tightly coiled tube lying adjacent to the testis and leading from the testis to the vas deferens. It is the site of sperm maturation and storage. The **ductus (vas) deferens (seminal duct)** is a long muscular tube leading from the epididymis up into the body cavity. It unites with the **ejaculatory duct** and empties its contents into the urethra. Coming from the seminal vesicles are the ejaculatory ducts. The urethra is the final tube. Remember from your study of the urinary system that the urethra has three sections. The prostatic urethra runs through the prostate gland; the intermediate urethra runs through the deep muscles of perineum; and the penile (spongy) urethra runs through the corpus spongiosum of the penis.

In addition, the male reproductive system has a series of glands that produce **seminal fluid**. The **seminal vesicles** are saclike structures attached to the ductus deferens near the base of the urinary bladder. They secrete an alkaline fluid that contains fructose. The **prostate gland** is a chestnut-shaped structure surrounding the urethra at the base of the urinary bladder. It secretes a milky, slightly acidic fluid that contains citric acid and enzymes. The **bulbourethral (Cowper's) glands** are small structures located inferior to the prostate gland. They secrete mucus to lubricate the tip of the penis during sexual arousal and an alkaline substance that neutralizes acid.

Semen is a combination of sperm cells and seminal fluid. One milliliter of semen can contain 120 million sperm.

Procedures

Female Reproductive System

Please locate and identify the following structures on all models and plaques that show them well. You are responsible for all structures whether the structure is numbered or not. Refer to the diagrams of the female reproductive system in your textbook if you need help. Study the structures, not the numbers! Structures grayed out in the table are not shown on that model.

Structure Name	Female Reproductive System Plaque	Menstrual Cycle Plaque	Mammary Glands Model
ovary	1	1	
uterine (Fallopian) tube, oviduct	2	6 & 7	
fimbriae of uterine tube	3	8	
uterus	5		
body of uterus		19	
cervix of uterus	6	21	
isthmus of uterus	7		
fundus of uterus	8	20	
myometrium		23	
endometrium		24	
vagina	9	22	
labium minus (plural = labia minora)	11		
labium majus (plural=labia majora)	12		
clitoris	13		
posterior fornix	14		
recto-uterine pouch	15		
corona radiata	16		
cytoplasm of ovum (egg)	18		
zona pellucida (green layer)	19		
cumulus oophorus	20		
urinary bladder	21		
urethra	22		
rectum	25		
anus	26		
round ligament of uterus	29		
ovarian ligament		9	
broad ligament		12	
suspensory ligament of ovary		18	
menstruation phase of endometrium		25	
implantation (of fertilized egg)		17	
primary oocyte in primordial follicle		A	
oocyte in primary follicle		B	

Structure Name	Female Reproductive System Plaque	Menstrual Cycle Plaque	Mammary Glands Model
mature ovarian (vesicular, Graafian) follicle		C	
ovulation of ovum		D	
corpus hemmorhagicum		E	
corpus luteum		F	
corpus albicans		G	
lymph nodes			1
pectoralis major muscle			2
adipose tissue			3
areola			4
lactiferous sinus (ampulla)			5
mammary ducts			6
mammary glands (composed of lobules containing alveoli)			7
suspensory (Cooper's) ligaments (represented by fine gray lines running through the fat)			8
lactiferous ducts			9

On the Female Reproductive Plaque the structures are about 1.5 times life size with spatial relationships anatomically correct. The egg is represented greatly enlarged, but incorrectly shows an organized nucleus.

On the Menstrual Cycle Plaque the uterus and associated organs are life size, but the ova outside the ovaries have been enlarged for visibility. The two ovaries in the central region of the model are three times life size. The sequence assumes a 28 day cycle with one follicle followed for the entire cycle in the model's center.

Male Reproductive System

Please locate and identify the following structures on all models and plaques that show them well. You are responsible for all structures whether the structure is numbered or not. Refer to the diagrams of the male reproductive system in your textbook if you need help. Study the structures, not the numbers! Structures grayed out in the table are not shown on that model.

Structure Name	Male Reproductive System Plaque	Male Urinary System Model	Male Reproductive Organs from Torso Model
testis	1		A
epididymis	2		B
ductus (vas) deferens	3	49	59
ampulla of ductus deferens	4		
seminal vesicle	5	50	E
ejaculatory duct	6		63
prostate gland	7	46	F
bulbourethral (Cowper's) gland	8		64
urethra	9	41	65
penis	10		G
corpus cavernosum of penis	11		67
corpus spongiosum of penis	12		69
glans penis	13		73
prepuce or foreskin of penis	15		72
scrotum	16		
head of sperm	17		
acrosome	(orange layer)		
nucleus	18		
midpiece	24		
mitochondria	26		
tail	27		
urinary bladder	28	37	
rectum	30		
anus	31		

On the Male Reproductive Plaque the structures are about 1.5 times life size with spatial relationships anatomically correct. The sperm is shown magnified 16,000 times actual size.

II. MICROSCOPIC ANATOMY OF THE REPRODUCTIVE SYSTEM

Introduction

Female Reproductive System

The **ovaries** are the site of female sex cell production. The outer surface of the ovary is covered with epithelium. Beneath the epithelium is the **tunica albuginea**, a zone with lots of reticular fibers and fibroblasts. Inside of the tunica albuginea is the ovarian cortex, the site of oocyte maturation. The developing oocytes are embedded in the **stroma,** a matrix of fibers, connective tissue cells, blood and lymph vessels, which continues throughout the ovary.

By the third month of life *in utero*, within the ovary of the female fetus, the primordial germ cells have given rise to oogonia. The **oogonia** are proliferating by mitosis, imbedded among early connective tissue cells which will form the stroma of the ovary. By the fifth month each fetal ovary will contain some 6,000,000 oogonia, with mitosis terminating within weeks. The oogonia are in compact clusters. The cell in the center of a cluster becomes a **primary oocyte** while those around it are thought to become the **follicular cells.** Many oogonia disappear. An oogonium becomes an oocyte by growing and beginning meiosis. Those cells becoming follicular cells flatten to form a thin capsule surrounding the oocyte. This is called a **primordial follicle**. At birth each primordial follicle will contain a **primary oocyte** arrested in prophase I of meiosis. No additional primary oocytes form after birth. By puberty several hundred thousand oocytes have degenerated, with those remaining resting late in the prophase I stage of meiosis. While a few oocytes mature to ovulation, most undergo **atresia**, the term describing the degenerative process resulting in an **atretic follicle**. Atresia of oocytes begins before birth, but proceeds most rapidly during a woman's reproductive years.

Each month after puberty, follicle stimulating hormone (FSH) from the anterior pituitary stimulates the cycle of a few primary oocytes to initiate maturation. As an oocyte enlarges, its surrounding follicular, squamous cells thicken becoming cuboidal in shape. It is now called a **primary follicle**. As the oocyte grows, the layer of cuboidal cells proliferate producing additional cell layers causing the follicle to enlarge. The follicular cells are also called **granulosa cells**. The inner most layer of cells around the oocyte, the **corona radiata** cells, secrete a coating called the **zona pellucida**, which will eventually appear as a thickened pink membrane. The zona is gel-like consisting of carbohydrates and glycoproteins and may contribute nutrition to the oocyte.

When the follicle attains several layers of **granulosa cells** around the primary oocyte, the unit will be called a developing or **secondary follicle**. A space, the **antrum**, develops between the follicular cells. It is being filled with **follicular fluid**. As the granulosa cells proliferate, the nearby stromal cells differentiate into a couple of layers called the **theca cells**. The theca and granulosa cells work together to produce the hormone estradiol (estrogen).

When the granulosa cells reach a thickness of 6 to 12 layers, a very large fluid filled antrum develops. At this stage the follicle is known as a **mature (vesicular** or **Graafian) follicle**. The "egg" is now known as a **secondary oocyte** as it has completed meiosis I and is starting meiosis II. The secondary oocyte is attached to one side of the follicle. The antrum is now filled with follicular fluid produced by the granulosa cells. The outer mound of granulosa cells surrounding the oocyte at the edge of the follicle is called the **cumulus oophorous**. These granulosa cells will be ovulated with the egg along with the corona radiata cells and the zona pellucida. The follicle has moved to the surface of the ovary. The follicular fluid is under some pressure and the overlying stroma thins out. Thus the mature follicle forms a bulge visible on the surface of the ovary.

A sudden surge of luteinizing hormone (LH) causes the follicle to rupture through the tunica albuginea. The rush of escaping follicular fluid washes the secondary oocyte and its surrounding cumulus oophorous from its follicle, resulting in **ovulation**. Chemical changes within the ovary immediately following ovulation inhibit other follicles that were maturing. At ovulation the egg is a secondary oocyte arrested in metaphase II of meiosis. Meiosis will not be completed unless fertilization occurs.

When the follicle is full of fluid and when hormone conditions are right, the egg will be ovulated from the follicle. Blood may enter the follicle upon ovulation and the structure remaining in the ovary is now called the **corpus hemorrhagicum.** The blood will be absorbed by the granulosa cells of the corpus hemorrhagicum. Theca and granulosa cells invade the remnant of the follicular antrum. Their growth converts the corpus hemorrhagicum into the **corpus luteum** (= yellow body). The theca and granulosa cells of the corpus luteum begin to secrete **progesterone** and **estrogen**. The hormone LH from the anterior pituitary gland contributes to the development and maintenance of the corpus luteum. If implantation occurs, **chorionic gonadotropic hormones (HCG)** from the developing placenta of the baby will maintain the corpus luteum and maintain its hormone production.

If implantation of the egg in the uterus does not occur, the corpus luteum will degenerate. This degeneration process is called **regression**. Eventually, the corpus luteum will regress to become the **corpus albicans** (= white body). The corpus albicans remains as a scar in the ovary for the rest of the female's life.

Sometime between 45 and 50 years after birth the ovaries run low of follicles to respond to the pituitary gonadotropins. With the ovaries unable to produce sufficient estrogen, **menopause** begins. A few follicles may persist until old age. At maturity the ovary will be twenty times larger than it was at birth. During the 30 or so years of reproductive life only about 400 primary oocytes will be ovulated. The last ones will have been sitting, waiting to complete prophase of the first meiotic division for some 45 years! This long duration of the first meiotic division is thought to contribute to the higher frequency of meiotic errors such as *nondisjunction*. This occurs when chromosomes fail to separate in meiosis and the resulting egg has extra or missing chromosomes. This can lead to the chromosome related birth defects often seen in children conceived by women over 35.

The uterus also undergoes changes each month. The uterine lining consists of a deeper layer called the **myometrium**, which contains smooth muscle and connective tissue and an inner lining called the **endometrium** which consists of **columnar epithelial cells**, **lamina propria** and **uterine glands**. During the first part of the cycle before ovulation has occurred in the ovary, the lamina propria is thinner and the uterine glands have a straight and smooth appearance. This time period is called the **follicular, pre-ovulatory phase** or **proliferative phase**. During the

secretory, post-ovulatory or **progravid phase,** progesterone from the corpus luteum has caused further thickening of the endometrium and a change in the structure of the glands. The uterine glands become deeper and have a tortuous (twisted) appearance.

Male Reproductive System

Seminiferous tubules are the site of **sperm (spermatozoa)** production in the male testes. Seminiferous tubules are constructed with a stratified epithelial tissue. The cells that surround the very edge of the tubule are large and are called **spermatogonia.** Spermatogonia will replicate by mitosis and the daughter cell will enter meiosis. The next sets of cells are in various stages of meiosis and are called **spermatocytes.** The primary spermatocytes are undergoing meiosis I, the secondary spermatocytes are undergoing meiosis II. The cells toward the lumen are small as they are now haploid and are called **spermatids.** Once they grow a tail, they are called spermatozoa or sperm.

There are also cells between the tubules. These are the **interstitial cells of Leydig**. These cells secrete **testosterone**. Testosterone is the male sex hormone. Testosterone regulates sperm production and male secondary sexual characteristics, such as hair growth, increased muscle mass, and deepening of the voice.

The epididymis is a portion of the male system of tubules for sperm delivery that lies on top of the testes like a coil. The epididymis is the site of sperm maturation and storage. Sperm may remain in storage here for at least a month, after which they are either expelled or degenerated and reabsorbed. The cells that line the tubule are **pseudostratified columnar epithelial cells.** They have long non-motile tufts of microvilli that are called **stereocilia.**

Procedures

Female Reproductive System

1. Obtain the slide labeled: **"Ovary, general structure"**. This slide of the ovary has follicles in varying stages of maturation.

2. Under the scanning objective, in the ovary's cortex look for the numerous **primordial follicles** near the edge of the ovary and the more mature follicles deeper in the organ. The follicles are embedded in the stroma.

3. Go to low and then high power. Identify the two or three cell layers of primordial follicles that can be seen just under the tunica albuginea. Each follicle contains a **primary oocyte** with a simple squamous epithelium surrounding it.

4. Locate a **primary follicle** with its layer of cuboidal to tall cuboidal follicular cells surrounding their primary oocyte.

5. Find a **secondary follicle** that has several cell layers surrounding the egg and a developing **antrum**.

6. Find an **atretic follicle**. If you cannot locate any, your instructor will show you some using photographs.

7. Scan your slide and see if you can see a **corpus hemorrhagicum**. If not, your instructor will show you a picture of one.

8. Draw a primordial, primary and secondary follicle in the POST-LAB OBSERVATIONS section. On the primordial and primary follicle, label the oocyte, and follicular cells. On the secondary follicle, label the theca cells, granulosa cells, corona radiata, zona pellucida, antrum and oocyte.

9. Obtain the slide labeled: **"Ovary, mature follicle cat"**.

10. Locate a **mature (vesicular, Graafian) follicle**. Observe at scanning, low and high power. Many sections through a large mature follicle will miss the oocyte and just reveal follicular fluid. In a mature vesicular ovarian follicle, the fluid completely fills the antrum and forces most of the granulosa cells over to the side of the follicle. Notice that some cells still surround the oocyte. Some of the slides are stained to emphasize the connective tissue fibers of the stroma by coloring them blue. On these slides the theca cells can be more easily distinguished from the rest of the ovarian stroma cells. The gel of the zona pellucida will also shrink and stain blue making it more easily observed.

11. Draw a mature (vesicular, Graafian) follicle in the POST-LAB OBSERVATIONS section and label oocyte, antrum, theca cells, granulosa cells, zona pellucida, corona radiata and cumulus oophorus.

12. Obtain a slide labeled: **"Cat ovary, corpus luteum"**.

13. The corpus luteum is a very large structure and almost fills the field under scanning power. It may look sort of "scalloped" in appearance. It begins to appear more scalloped as it undergoes regression.

14. You may be able to find a corpus albicans on your slide. If not, your instructor will show you one on the 35 mm slides.

15. Make a sketch of a corpus luteum in the OBSERVATIONS section.

16. Obtain a slide labeled: **"Uterus, human foll. phase"**.

17. On scanning power, locate the endometrium and the myometrium. The endometrium is a combination of simple columnar epithelial cell and the underlying connective tissue, the lamina propria. The myometrium is layers of smooth muscle.

18. On scanning, low and then high power, locate a uterine gland, they appear as purple circles. Note that the gland is composed of epithelial cells. Note that the walls of the gland are smooth.

19. Make a sketch of the uterine glands in the pre-ovulatory phase in the POST-LAB OBSERVATIONS section. Label endometrium, myometrium and uterine glands.

20. Obtain a slide labeled: **"Uterus, human progravid phase"**.

21. On scanning power, locate the endometrium and the myometrium. Note on scanning power that the endometrium is much more extensive than the pre-ovulatory phase.

22. On scanning, low and then high power, locate a uterine gland. Note that the walls of the gland are longer and twisted. Be able to distinguish pre-ovulatory phase from post-ovulatory phase under a microscope.

23. Make a sketch of the glands in post-ovulatory phase in the POST-LAB OBSERVATIONS section. Label endometrium, myometrium and uterine glands.

Male Reproductive System

1. Obtain a slide labeled **"Spermatogenesis, rat testis"**.

2. On scanning power, note that this organ consists of tubules. These are the seminiferous tubules. Focus on a single tubule under scanning, low and then high power.

3. Identify the spermatogonia, spermatocytes, spermatids and sperm (spermatozoa) within the seminiferous tubules. It is difficult to tell the primary and secondary spermatocytes apart so just know that they are spermatocytes. In the rat testis, the rat sperm heads have a somewhat "hook-like" shape.

4. Find the interstitial cells (of Leydig) between the seminiferous tubules. Many times there are also blood vessels in the space between the tubules.

5. Make a sketch of the rat testis in the POST-LAB OBSERVATIONS section. Label the interstitial cells (of Leydig), a spermatogonium, a spermatocyte, a spermatid and a sperm.

6. Obtain a slide labeled **"Epididymis, human"**.

7. Note on scanning power that when sectioned it consists of many circles. These are the tubules of the epididymis. Focus on a single tubule under scanning, low and then high power.

8. At high power, observe that the tubules are made of pseudostratified columnar epithelium. On the surface of the cells there are projections called stereocilia. Stereocilia are not true cilia, but instead are microvilli. In the lumen, clumps of sperm may be seen.

9. Draw a tubule of the epididymis in the POST-LAB OBSERVATIONS section. Label the pseudostratifed columnar cells and stereocilia.

Reproductive System Microscopic Structures

Structure Name – Ovary
primordial follicles
atretic follicle
primary follicle
secondary follicle
mature (vesicular, Graafian) follicle
primary oocyte
follicular cells
antrum
granulosa cells
theca cells
corona radiata
zona pellucida
corpus luteum
corpus albicans
Structure Name – Uterus
endometrium
simple columnar epithelium
lamina propria
myometrium
uterine glands
Structure Name – Testes
seminiferous tubules
spermatogonium
spermatocyte
spermatid
sperm
interstitial cells (of Leydig)
Structure Name – Epididymis
pseudostratifed columnar cells
stereocilia

Name_____

A. Refer to your textbook and diagram the steps of spermatogenesis.

B. What are some functions of testosterone?

C. What is the function of the epididymis?

D. Define:

    1. ovarian follicle

    2. corpus luteum

    3. atresia

    4. endometrium

E. Refer to your textbook and list the stages of the ovarian cycle.

F. List the stages (phases) of the menstrual cycle from your textbook

From the History:

G. Which anatomist first described the uterine tube? _____

H. GROSS ANATOMY

Female Reproductive System

1. Label all structures shown.

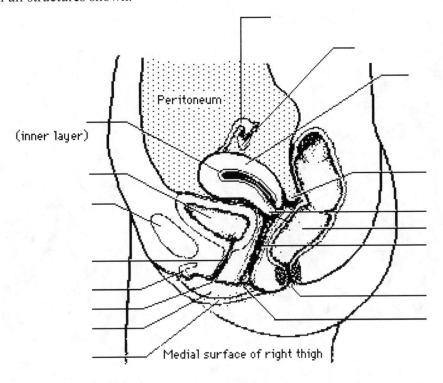

Figure 1. Female pelvis, sagittal section.

2. Mammary glands. Label all structures shown in the center. The lines lead to the same structures in both diagrams when you place the names in the middle.

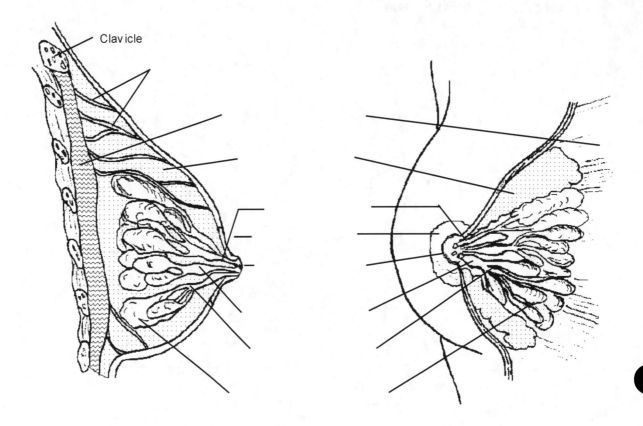

Figure 2. Female breast in sagittal section and cut away from medial anterior view.

3. Label all structures shown. Body wall, digestive system, and scrotum are not shown.

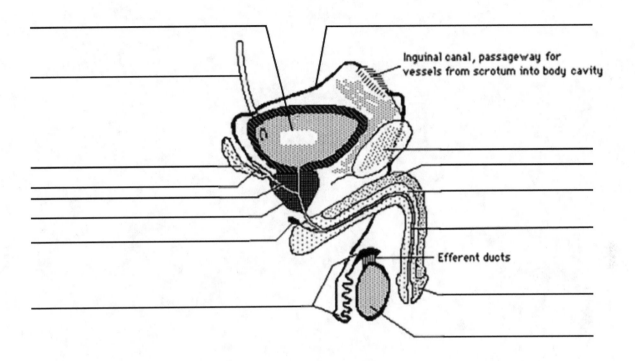

Figure 3. Male reproductive system, sagittal section.

DEVELOPMENT

HISTORY

Diocles, who practiced medicine in Athens in the fourth century BC developed a theory of embryology that was close to correct. He believed that the new child came from a fusion of the "seed" of both sexes. This was in contrast to Aristotle's later claim that the child was created from the female menstrual blood with no contribution of the mother and even the father did not contribute "seed" but rather somehow gave the baby its soul. Leonardo da Vinci is considered the father of embryology although his notebooks on the subject were lost until 1911. Delivery of a baby was done by midwives for centuries, or if there was difficulty, by a male physician reaching under a sheet. In the mid-1800s Ludwig Semmelweis discovered that the death rate due to women being attended by physicians in childbirth was twice as high as deaths due to attendance by midwives. He succeeded in finally getting physicians to wash their hands and use an antiseptic. Julius Caesar was said to be delivered by an incision in the abdominal wall, but caesarian sections were only performed in case of the death of the mother until 1836.

OBJECTIVES

1. To study the early stages of cleavage and embryonic development.
2. To observe the changes in the anatomy of the mother and fetus which occur during development.

I. THE EARLY EMBRYO

Introduction

Development involves the growth of an individual from a single fertilized egg into its final recognizable form at birth or hatching. This process is a complex one, involving **mitosis** and subsequent specialization or **differentiation** of the resulting cells. Differentiation requires regulation and inactivation of certain portions of the DNA within each cell. The study of development includes the process of **fertilization** of the egg by the sperm and early cell divisions known as **cleavage** (which means that the size of the cells does not increase after division). In mammals (as well as some sharks) it also involves **implantation** in the uterine wall, growth of the **placenta** and the **embryo** and growth of the **fetus**.

Development begins with the process of fertilization, the merger of the secondary oocyte (ovum) and a sperm. Fertilization normally occurs in the uterine tube within 12 to 24 hours after ovulation. For fertilization to occur a sperm must penetrate the corona radiata and zona pellucida around the oocyte. Once the sperm penetrates the oocyte, the oocyte rapidly completes meiosis II. At this time the chromosomes of the oocyte are called the **female pronucleus** and the **male pronucleus** is the chromosomes from the sperm. Once the male and female pronuclei combine, the fertilized ovum is called a **zygote** or one cell embryo.

The early cell divisions of the zygote are known as **cleavage**. During the cleavages the embryo remains in the zona pellucida and the cells become progressively smaller. A **two cell embryo** is produced by the first cleavage about 30 hours after fertilization. The second cleavage occurs on Day 2 and produces a **four cell embryo**. The **sixteen cell embryo** is produced on day 3. Once an embryo has sixteen cells or more it is called a **morula** (*morus* = L. mulberry), which is a solid ball of cells. The morula will transform into a **blastocyst (blastula)**, a hollow ball of cells with a fluid filled cavity, the blastocele, on day 5-6. In primitive animals like starfish, the blastula is a single layer of cells with an inner blastocele. In vertebrates, there is an outer layer of cells, the **trophoblast**, the blastocele, and an **inner cell mass**, an extra clump of cells to the side of the blastocele, which would eventually be forming the new animal. The blastocyst will enter the uterine cavity around day 5.

Implantation is the attachment of a blastocyst to the endometrium of the uterus. It occurs approximately seven to eight days after fertilization. Before the embryo can implant into the wall of the uterus, it must shed its zona pellucida in a process called **hatching**. Following implantation the endometrium is known as the decidua. There are three regions of decidua. The **decidua basalis** is the layer directly under the embryo and will become the maternal part of the placenta. The **decidua capsularis** covers the embryo and is located between the embryo and the uterine cavity. The **decidua parietalis** lines the noninvolved areas of the entire pregnant uterus. As the pregnancy progresses the decidua capsularis becomes part of the decidua parietalis. During labor and delivery, all of decidua is shed from the uterus with the placenta.

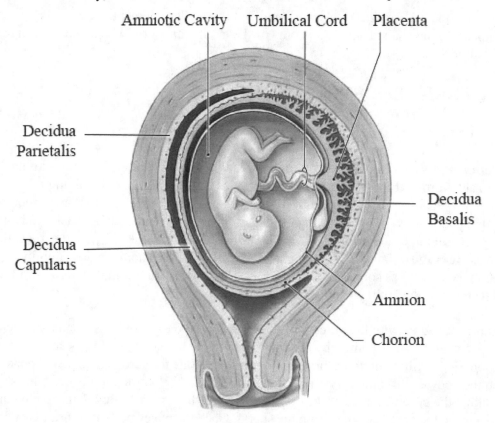

Figure 1. Decidua layers of the Uterus after Implantation.

The trophoblast of the blastocyst will eventually form the embryonic membranes, the chorion and amnion. The **chorion** becomes the embryonic contribution to the placenta. The **amnion** is a thin, protective membrane that initially overlies only the embryo on one side. Eventually the amnion surrounds the entire embryo creating the **amniotic cavity**, which contains amnionic fluid. The **yolk sac** is a structure formed in the former blastocele.

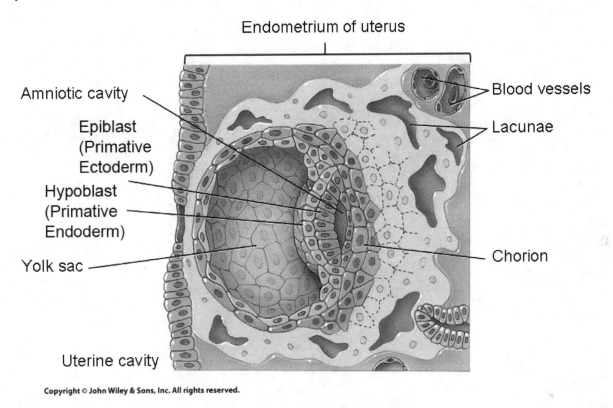

Figure 2. Frontal section through endometrium of uterus showing blastocyst, about 9 days after fertilization.

Between the amnionic cavity and the yolk sac, the inner cell mass forms the bilaminar embryonic disc. The two layers of the bilaminar embryonic disc are the primitive **endoderm** (hypoblast), which borders the yolk sac and the primitive **ectoderm** (epiblast), which borders the amnionic cavity. During the third week of development, cells from the ectoderm push into the area between the ectoderm and endoderm forming a third layer, the **mesoderm**. This process is called **gastrulation**. In primitive animals the gastrulation process is different. In starfish, a **gastrula** is formed when a group of cells on one side of the embryo (yellow) divides more rapidly and pushes into the blastocoele, forming the ectoderm and endoderm.

The cells of the embryonic layers will eventually form all the tissues of the body. A few of the structures that the ectoderm will become are the epidermis of skin and the nervous system. The endoderm develops into the epithelial linings of the body, and the mesoderm develops into muscles, heart, bone and other connective tissues.

After implantation, development proceeds rapidly with massive cell division and differentiation. During the fourth week of development, the early nervous system begins, the early ear, the otic placode, is seen, the early eye, the lens placode, develops and the upper limb buds and the lower limb buds appear by the end of the fourth week.

Procedures

Please locate and identify the following structures on all models and plaques that show them well. You are responsible for all structures whether the structure is numbered or not. Study the structures, not the numbers! Structures grayed out in the table are not shown on that model.

Structure Name	Embryo Models	Human Development Series	Cell to Embryo Plaque
ovum		Model 1	A & 2, 22
corona radiata		Model 1 (1)	24
zona pellucida		Model 1 (2) Model 2 (1)	23
spermatozoa (sperm)		Model 1 (5)	25
fertilization		Model 2	B & 10
zygote	Model 1	Models 2-6	
female pronucleus		Model 1 (4) Model 2 (4) Model 4 (1) Model 5 (1)	
male pronucleus		Model 3 (3) Model 4 (2) Model 5 (2)	
cleavage			12
two cell embryo	Model 2	Model 7	
four cell embryo	Model 3	Model 8	C
eight cell embryo	Model 4		
sixteen cell embryo	Model 5	Model 9	
morula	Models 5 & 6	Model 9	D & 13
blastula (blastocyst)	Models 7 & 8	Model 10	E
blastocyst cavity (blastocoele)		Model 10 (2)	
gastrula	Models 9 & 10		
21 day embryo			F
five week embryo			G
trophoblast		Model 10 (1&6)	29
chorion		Model 11 (9)	38
chorionic villi		Model 12 (10) Model 13 (8)	39
embryonic blood vessels		Model 13 (8&10)	
bilaminar embryonic disc			27

Structure Name	Embryo Models	Human Development Series	Cell to Embryo Plaque
ectoderm		Model 10 (4) Model 11 (1) Model 12 (1)	
endoderm		Model 10 (3) Model 11 (3) Model 12 (3)	
mesoderm		Model 12 (2)	
amniotic cavity		Model 10 (5) Model 11 (2) Model 12 (5) Model 13 (3)	26
amnion		Model 13 (4)	31
yolk sac		Model 11 (4) Model 12 (6) Model 13 (1)	28 & 33
embryo			30
developing umbilical cord		Model 13(2)	40
developing heart		Model 12 (7)	32 & 46
forebrain			41
eye			44
developing outer ear			45
tail			49
digital rays			50
toe rays			51
implantation of blastocyst			15
uterus			
body of uterus			16
fundus of uterus			17
myometrium of uterus			18
cervix			19
endometrium			20
decidua basalis		Model 10 (7) Model 13 (7)	
decidua capsularis		Model 11 (13) Model 13 (6)	
decidua parietalis			
maternal spiral arteries		Model 11 (12) Model 13 (9)	
ovary			1
oocyte in primary follicle			3
mature (vesicular, Graafian) follicle			4

Structure Name	Embryo Models	Human Development Series	Cell to Embryo Plaque
ovulation			5
corpus hemorrhagicum			
oocyte (ovum) at ovulation			8
corpus luteum			6
corpus albicans			7
fimbriae of uterine tube			9
uterine tube (Fallopian tube, oviduct)			11
vagina			21

The brown embryo models on the black stands represent the earliest development of the embryo. While these models are based on studies of sea stars (starfish) they are very similar to those of vertebrates up through model 8. In the human, the zygote and embryo up through 4-5 days, model 6, would be surrounded by the remnants of the zona pellucida and corona radiata, which is not on the models. The size of the embryo does not increase until after reaching the uterus. Until then the cells get smaller with each division as they partition the existing cytoplasm among the daughter cells.

II. PREGNANCY SERIES, EMBRYO and FETUS

Introduction

From the week five to eight the developing human is still called an **embryo**. During the fifth week there is rapid brain development and considerable head growth. The head grows even larger in relation to the trunk, there is substantial limb growth, the neck and truck begin to straighten, and the heart is now four-chambered during the sixth week. During the seventh week the various regions of the limbs become distinct and the beginnings of the digits appear. By the end of the eighth week all regions of the limbs are apparent, the digits are distinct, the eyelids come together, the tail disappears, and the external genitals begin to differentiate.

When one can tell what the organism is to become, it is then called a **fetus**. By about 8 weeks after conception the developing human has attained enough distinct features to be recognized as a human.

Procedures

Examine the Somso life size model Series Showing Pregnancy and locate the structures listed. There are eight models in various stages of pregnancy showing the uterus with the embryo or fetus.

Structure Name	Pregnancy Series Models
Uterus with embryo in first month	Model 1
Uterus with embryo in second month	Model 2
Uterus with fetus in third month	Model 3
Uterus with fetus in fourth to fifth month, prone position	Model 4
Uterus with fetus in fifth month, breech position	Model 5
Uterus with fetus in fifth month, dorsal position	Model 6
Uterus with fetus in seventh month, normal position	Model 7
Uterus with twin fetuses in fifth month	Model 8
uterus	1
placenta	2
umbilical cord	3
cervix	4
vagina	5
uterine tube (oviduct, Fallopian tube)	6
fimbriae	7
ovary	8
broad ligament of uterus	9
embryo/fetus	10
decidua capsularis/decidua parietalis	11
inner wall of the amniotic sac or amnion	12
uterine cavity	13
cervix	14
external os	15
round ligament of uterus	16
internal os	17
decidua parietalis	18
umbilical arteries	19
umbilical vein	20

The wall between numbers 11 & 13 consists of three layers: innermost is the amnion, then the chorion (thick reddish brown layer) and outermost layer, the decidua capsularis.

III. FETAL DEVELOPMENT

Introduction

During the fetal period, tissue and organs that developed during the embryonic period grow and differentiate. The rate of body growth is remarkable. A few major highlights of the fetal period include: the heartbeat can be detected between week 9 and 12, gender is distinguishable from external genitals by week 12, fetal movements are commonly felt by the mother by week 20, and the lungs start producing surfactant by week 24.

During the fetal period the **placenta** will complete its development. It will fully form during 3rd month. The placenta is a combination of the **chorionic villi** from fetus and the decidua basalis from the mother. Chorionic villi are projections of the chorion that eventually contain blood filled capillaries. These blood capillaries lead to the umbilical cord. Within the umbilical cord there is one **umbilical vein** carrying oxygenated blood to the fetus from the chorionic villi and two **umbilical arteries** carrying deoxygenated blood to the chorionic villi in the placenta. The chorionic villi extend into maternal blood filled intervillous spaces in the decidua basalis. The maternal and fetal blood vessels do not join and their blood does not mix. Oxygen, nutrients, and wastes diffuse between the chorionic villi and the maternal blood pool. After the birth of the baby, placenta detaches from the uterus and becomes the afterbirth.

Because during the fetal period the fetal lungs need minimal blood flow, most of the blood is diverted away from the lungs. In the fetal circulatory system, blood flows directly from the right atrium to the left atrium through a hole in the interatrial septum called the **foramen ovale**. Blood leaving the right ventricle through the pulmonary trunk can be diverted to the aorta via a vessel called the **ductus arteriosis**. Both of these structures will close at the time of birth. The **fossa ovale** and the **ligamentun arteriosis** are the remains of the foramen ovale and ductus arteriosis, respectively.

At the end of the fetal period, the pregnant female will go into labor, which is the process of expelling the fetus. True labor begins when uterine contractions occur at regular intervals, usually producing pain. There are three stages of labor. 1. Dilation, which can last 6 to 12 hours. During this stage there are regular contractions of the uterus, the amniotic sac will rupture, and the cervix will dilate to 10cm. 2. Expulsion, which can last 10 minutes to several hours. The baby moves through the birth canal during this stage. 3. Placental, 30 minutes. The afterbirth is expelled by uterine contractions. The uterus continues to contract to constrict blood vessels that were torn, which reduces the possibility of hemorrhage.

Procedures

Please locate and identify the following structures on the plaques that show them well. Study the structures, not the numbers! Structures grayed out in the table are not shown on that model.

Structure Name	Four Month Fetus Plaque	Full Term Fetus Plaque	Full Term Fetus Plaque Placenta
6 week embryo	A		
8 week fetus	B		
10 week fetus	C		
12 week fetus	D		
14 week fetus	E		
16 week fetus	F		
full-term fetus		1	
myometrium	1	5	16
cervix	2	6	

Structure Name	Four Month Fetus Plaque	Full Term Fetus Plaque	Full Term Fetus Plaque Placenta
amnion/amniotic sac	3	4	4
amniotic fluid			18
placenta	4	3	
chorionic villus			7 & 8
intervillous cavity (filled with maternal blood pool)			9
maternal venule			10
spiral maternal arteriole			12
decidua basalis			14 & 15
umbilical cord	5	2	1
umbilical vein			2
umbilical arteries			3
vagina	6	11	
vaginal orifice	7	12	
labium minus (pl. labia minora)	8	13	
labium majus (pl. labia majora)	9	14	
urinary bladder	10	19	
urethra	11	20	
pubic symphysis	12	16	
posterior fornix	13	10	
rectum	15	23	
clitoris		15	

On the Hubbard Four Month Fetus plaque, the sizes of the embryo and fetuses are actual size.

Note that the umbilical vein is red because it carries oxygen rich blood from the placenta, and that the umbilical arteries are blue because they carry oxygen poor blood to the placenta.

On the Full Term Fetus plaque notice the compression of the urinary bladder and the partial dilation of the cervix. The Placenta Detail is a semi-diagrammatic enlargement showing details of placental structure.

A. Define the following:

    1. fertilization:

    2. cleavage:

    3. amnion:

    4. morula:

    5. blastocyst:

    6. implantation:

B. Describe the following structures found in fetal circulation:

    1. foramen ovale:

    2. ductus arteriosus:

C. List the three primary germ layers of the embryo. With each, list two or more adult structures which are derived from each layer.

D. Describe the appearance of the embryo after 4 weeks of life (21-25 days). (What obvious structures are present?)

E. Describe what happens during the three stages of labor:

From History:

F. How did Semmelweis reduce childbirth deaths?

I. THE EARLY EMBRYO

A. Match the embryo picture with its name.

A.

B.

C.

D.

E.

One cell embryo   _____

Two cell embryo   _____

Four cell embryo   _____

Morula   _____

Blastocyst   _____

II. PREGNANCY SERIES, EMBRYO and FETUS

A. Label the different birth positions.

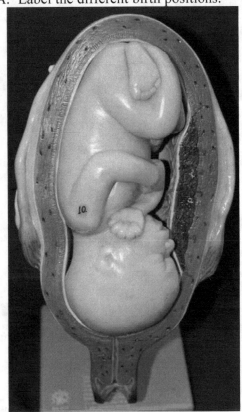
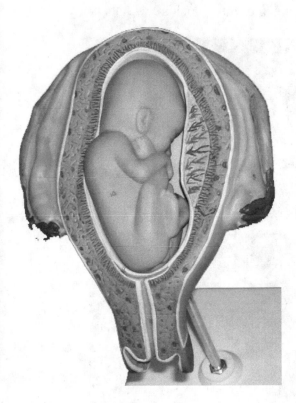

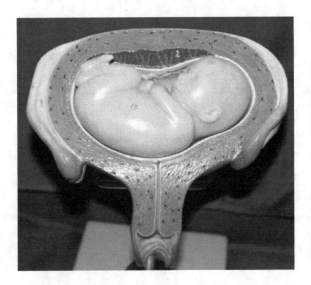
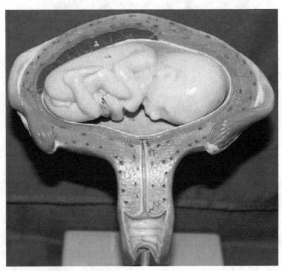

III. FETAL DEVELOPMENT

A. Label the ages of embryos and fetuses from the Four Month Fetus plaque

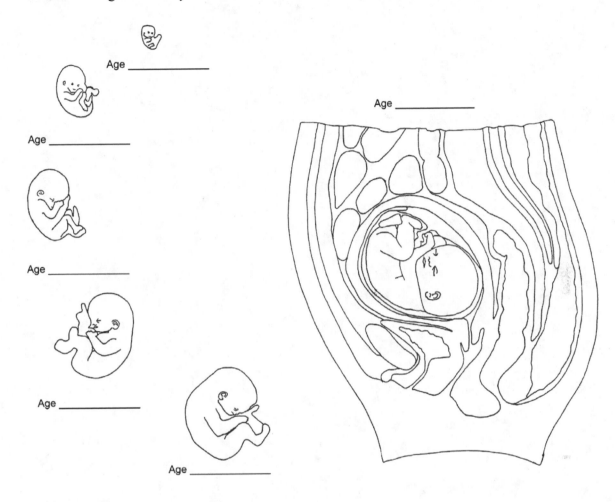

Age _____

Age _____

Age _____

Age _____

Age _____

Age _____

Age _____

Page Deliberately Left Blank

Leica Binocular Microscope
MCC Human Anatomy and Physiology Labs

PROCEDURES

A. CARE OF MICROSCOPE

1. Before going to the cabinet to get your microscope, clear a generous area at your work space of all unneeded paraphernalia. Accidents with microscopes are more frequent and your efficiency is impaired when you attempt to work in crowded quarters.
2. Select the scope which corresponds to your seat number from the cabinet. Grasp the arm of the microscope with one hand and place your other hand under the base as you carefully lift the scope from the shelf. Using both hands, carry the scope in an upright position to your desk. NEVER attempt to carry two microscopes at one time or carry a scope in one hand swinging at your side. IF YOU BREAK IT, YOU BUY IT!
3. The lenses of the microscope should be cleaned with each use. Lenses which are dirty, wet, or scratched lower the efficiency of the microscope. USE ONLY CLEAN COTTON SWABS to polish the lens surface. Always lubricate the glass with lens cleaner solution when wiping with the cotton swab. NEVER use a paper towel, your handkerchief, or other paper or cloth to clean a microscope lens. If you have trouble, consult the instructor.
4. Always plug in and unplug the power cord by grasping the plug end, not the wire.
5. At the end of a days work follow this procedure BEFORE PUTTING THE MICROSCOPE AWAY:
   a. Turn off the lamp.
   b. CENTER the mechanical stage. The stage should be clean and dry.
   c. Put the scanning objective in place.
   d. Loop the power cord neatly around the cord holder at the back of the microscope.
   e. CLEAN all lenses.

B. USING THE l\1ICROSCOPE

1. With the microscope centered in front of you, the back of the base should be a short distance in from the front of the desk. The eyepieces will be toward you and the arm to the rear. Your chair height and back are adjustable. Position yourself and the scope so you can look into the eyepieces comfortably.
2. You must adjust for the interocular distance of your pupils.
   a. With the scanning objective in place, turn the lamp on.
   b. Looking through the eyepieces you see white circles of light. Grasp the binocular tubes and pivot moving the circles of light until they exactly overlap and you only see one with both eyes open.
3. To better see the sample on the slide, adjust the amount of light that goes through the slide by adjusting the iris diaphragm under the stage. Look at the iris diaphragm to see where your iris diaphragm should be set at each magnification.
4. The oil immersion lens (100X) will not be used in Bio202.

III. MICROSCOPIC STRUCTURE OF CARDIAC MUSCLE

A. Sketch a longitudinal view of cardiac muscle tissue noting the intercalated discs, striations, and nuclei.

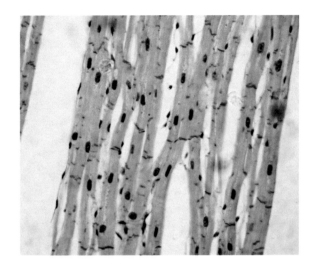

Page deliberately left blank

II. MICROSCOPIC STRUCTURE OF THE BLOOD VESSELS

A. Sketch **both** an artery and vein in cross section based on the microscope slides and label the tunica interna, tunica media and tunica externa.

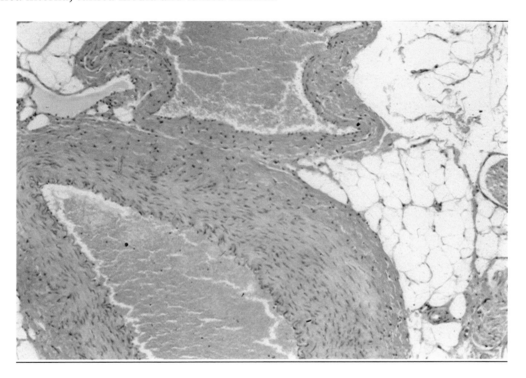

III. MICROSCOPIC STRUCTURE OF LIVING VESSELS

A. Draw and describe in words what you saw when you looked at the goldfish tail circulation under the microscope.

B. Could you distinguish arterioles from venules during the observation?

C. Does the blood flow at the same rate in all the vessels, or does it appear to move faster in some and slower in others?

IV. MICROSCOPIC STRUCTURE OF LYMPH VESSELS

A. Draw a lymph vessel and valve based on your microscopic observation. Label the valve.

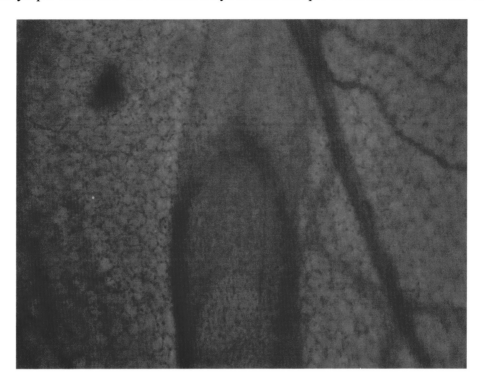

V. DEMONSTRATION OF VENOUS VALVES

A. Describe in words what happened during this exercise.

POST-LAB OBSERVATIONS

II. MICROSCOPIC ANATOMY

A. Obtain the slide labeled **"Pseudostratified ciliated columnar epithelium"**. Sketch a section of the tracheal wall. Label lumen, mucosa, ciliated pseudostratified columnar epithelium, lamina propria, submucosa, tracheal glands, hyaline cartilage, chondrocytes, lacunae, matrix, perichondrium and adventitia

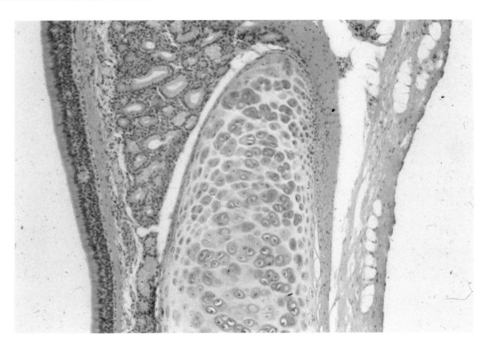

B. Obtain the slide labeled "Lung". Sketch an alveolus and a capillary from the slide under high
   power. Label capillary, blood cells, alveolus, and simple squamous epithelium.

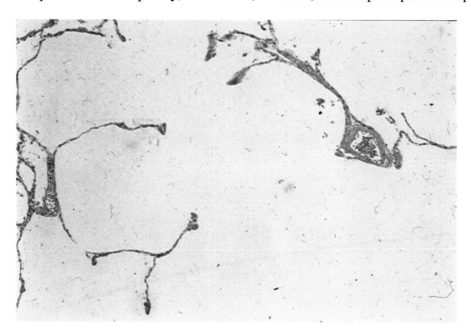

POST-LAB OBSERVATIONS

II. MICROSCOPIC ANATOMY OF THE URINARY SYSTEM

A. From the slide of the kidney, make a sketch of a renal corpuscle below and label the glomerulus, capsular space and parietal layer of Bowman's (glomerular) capsule.

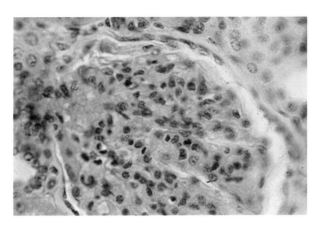

B. Sketch and label the proximal convoluted tubules and distal convoluted tubules of the nephron from the slide.

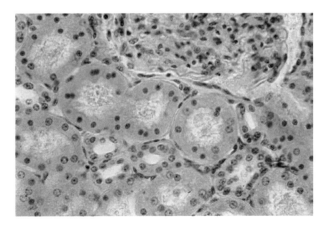

C. Draw the juxtaglomerular apparatus, as seen on the demo scope. Label the macula densa and the juxtaglomerular cells.

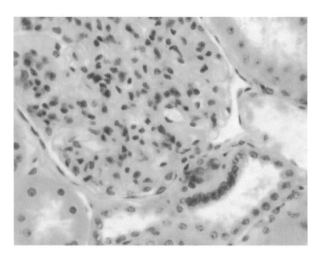

D. Draw a cross section of the ureter and label: mucosa, transitional epithelium, lamina propria, and muscularis (inner longitudinal and outer circular layers). Draw the adventitia (fibrous coat), if it is present. Include details of the transitional epithelium of the mucosa showing number of cell layers and their shape.

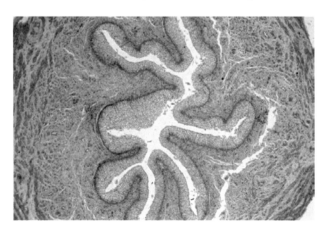

POST- LAB OBSERVATIONS

II. MICROSCOPIC ANATOMY OF THE DIGESTIVE SYSTEM

Complete this portion while reading the description in the lab and looking through the microscope.

A. Salivary gland slide. Draw and label a single mucous acinous, a serous acinous and an excretory duct below.

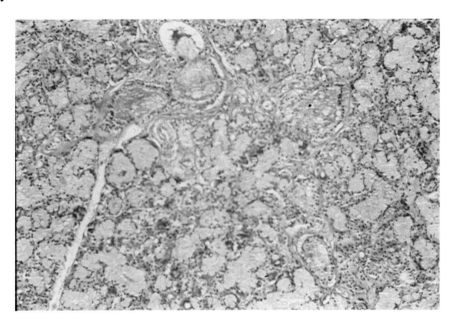

B. Stomach slide. One drawing done at scanning power should include all layers. Label: mucosa, muscularis mucosa, submucosa, muscularis externa, serosa. On a second drawing showing a high power view of the mucosa. Label: simple columnar epithelium, gastric pits, gastric glands, chief cells, and parietal cells.

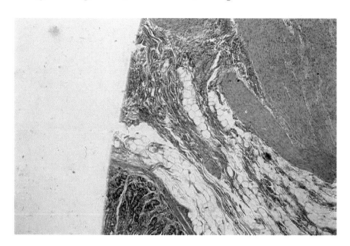

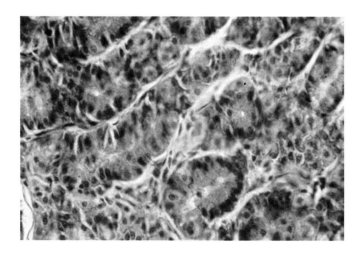

C. Duodenum slide. Draw and label a sketch of the duodenum below. Label these structures: mucosa (include simple columnar epithelial cells and lamina propria), muscularis mucosa, submucosa, circular layer of smooth muscle, longitudinal layer of smooth muscle, visceral peritoneum, intestinal glands (crypts), duodenal (Brunner's) glands.

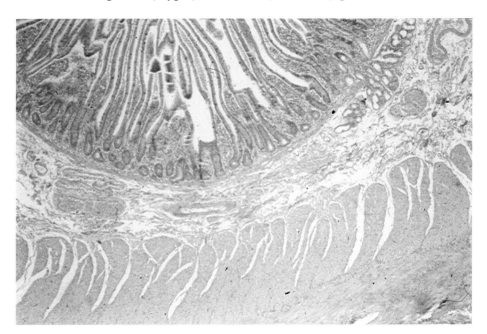

D. Ileum slide. Draw and label a sketch of the ileum below. Include these structures: mucosa, muscularis mucosae, submucosa, muscularis externa, serosa, simple columnar epithelium, goblet cells, lamina propria, villi, intestinal glands, lymph nodules (Peyer's patches).

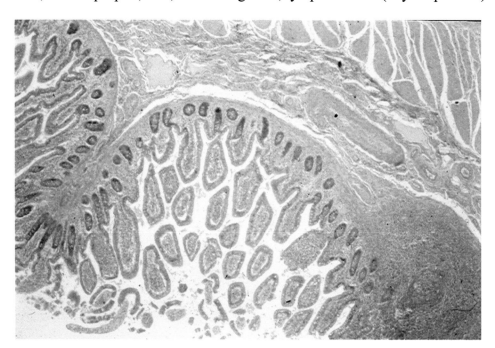

PRE-LAB QUESTIONS   Name_____

A. Fill in the table with each hormone's major functions and the gland that secretes the hormone:

Hormone	Function	Gland that Secretes Hormone
Growth Hormone		
Prolactin		
Thyroxine		
Parathyroid hormone (PTH, Parathormone)		
Cortisol		
Aldosterone		
Epinephrine		
Oxytocin		

B. Where is oxytocin actually **produced**? _____

POST-LAB OBSERVATIONS

II. MICROSCOPIC ANATOMY OF THE ENDOCRINE SYSTEM

A. Make a sketch of a pancreatic islet and several acini below. Label both the pancreatic islet and the acini.

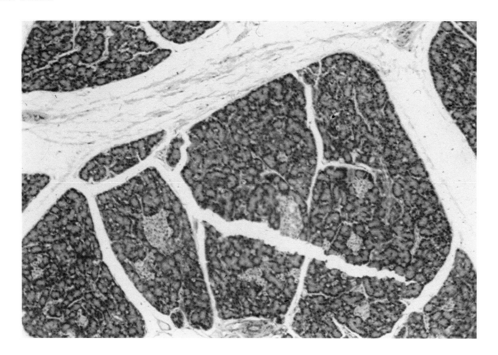

POST-LAB OBSERVATIONS

II. MICROSCOPIC ANATOMY OF THE REPRODUCTIVE SYSTEM

Read lab directions before trying to draw structures below.

Female Reproductive System

A. Using the two ovary slides, draw a primordial and primary follicle. Label follicular cells and primary oocyte.

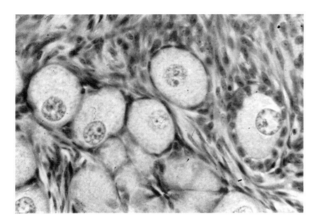

B. Using the two ovary slides, draw a secondary follicle. Label theca cells, granulosa cells, corona radiata, zona pellucida, and oocyte.

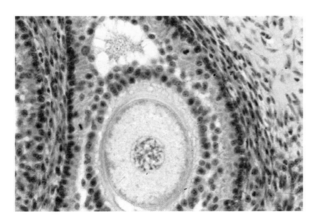

A. Using the slide labeled **"Ovary, mature follicle, cat."**, Draw a mature (vesicular or Graafian) follicle. Label oocyte, antrum, theca cells, granulosa cells, zona pellucida, corona radiata and cumulus oophorus.

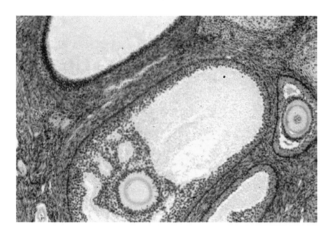

B. Using the slide labeled **"Cat ovary, corpus luteum"**, draw and label a corpus luteum.

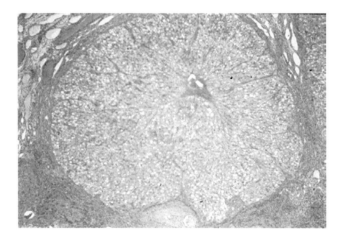

C. Using the slide labeled **"Uterus, human foll. phase"** make a sketch of the uterine wall showing glands. Label: endometrium, myometrium and uterine glands.

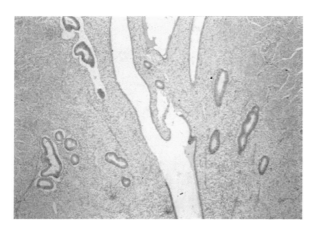

D. Using the slide labeled **"Uterus, human, progravid phase"**, make a sketch of the uterine wall showing glands. Label: endometrium, myometrium and uterine glands.

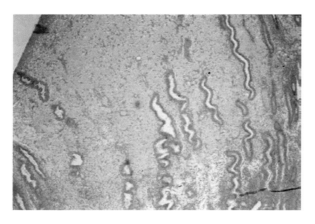

Male Reproductive System

A. Using the slide labeled **"Spermatogenesis, rat testis"**, make a sketch of interstitial cells (Leydig cells) and a seminiferous tubule below. Label: interstitial cells (of Leydig), a spermatogonium, a spermatocyte, a spermatid and a sperm.

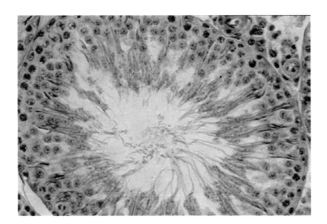

B. Using the slide labeled **"Epididymis, human"**, make a sketch of an epididymis tubule below. Label stereocilia and pseudostratified columnar cells.

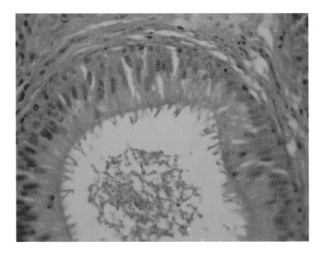